The War of Heru and Set

The Epic Struggle of Good and Evil
for control of the World and the Human Soul

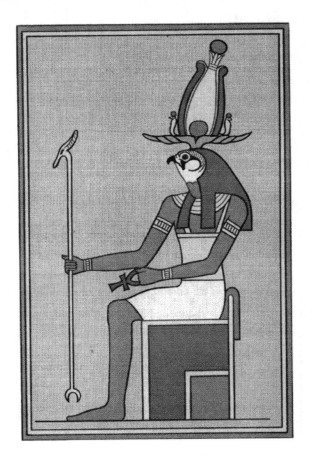

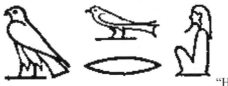

"Heru the King)

P. O. Box 570459
Miami, Florida, 33257
(305) 378-6253 Fax: (305) 378-6253

© 1998-2001, The King of Egypt
© 2002 By Sema Institute of Yoga and Reginald Muata Abhaya Ashby
© 2005 The War of Heru and Set- the War of Life/King of Egypt

All rights reserved. No part of this book may be used or reproduced in any manner whatsoever without written permission (address above) except in the case of brief quotations embodied in critical articles and reviews. All inquiries may be addressed to the address above.

The author is available for group lectures and individual counseling. For further information contact the publisher.

Ashby, Muata
The War of Heru and Set- the War of Life/King of Egypt ISBN: 1-884564-44-5

Library of Congress Cataloging in Publication Data

1 Comparative Religion 2 History 3 Culture, 4 Egyptian Philosophy.

Sema Institute

Website
www.Egyptianyoga.com

The Book

THE WAR OF LIFE

is inspired by the Original Research Which Was presented in the Book

RESURRECTING OSIRIS:
The Path of Mystical Awakening and The Keys to Immortality
By
Dr. Muata Ashby

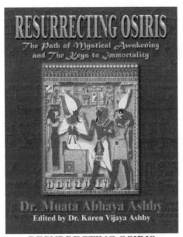

RESURRECTING OSIRIS
The path of Mystical Awakening and the Keys to Immortality

NEW REVISED AND EXPANDED EDITION!

The Ancient Sages created stories based on human and superhuman beings whose struggles, aspirations, needs and desires ultimately lead them to discover their true Self. The myth of Isis, Osiris and Heru is no exception in this area. While there is no one source where the entire story may be found, pieces of it are inscribed in various ancient temples walls, tombs, steles and papyri. For the first time available, the complete myth of Osiris, Isis and Heru has been compiled from original Ancient Egyptian, Greek and Coptic Texts. This epic myth has been richly illustrated with reliefs from the temple of Heru at Edfu, the temple of Isis at Philae, the temple of Osiris at Abydos, the temple of Hathor at Denderah and various papyri, inscriptions and reliefs.

Discover the myth which inspired the teachings of the *Shetaut Neter* (Egyptian Mystery System - Egyptian Yoga) and the Egyptian Book of Coming Forth By Day. Also, discover the three levels of Ancient Egyptian Religion, how to understand the mysteries of the Tuat or Astral World and how to discover the abode of the Supreme in the Amenta, *The Other World*.

The ancient religion of Osiris, Isis and Heru, if properly understood, contains all of the elements necessary to lead the sincere aspirant to attain immortality through inner self-discovery. This volume presents the entire myth and explores the main mystical themes and rituals associated with the myth for understating human existence, creation and the way to achieve spiritual emancipation - *Resurrection*. The Osirian myth is so powerful that it influenced and is still having an effect on the major world religions. Discover the origins and mystical meaning of the Christian Trinity, the Eucharist ritual and the ancient origin of the birthday of Jesus Christ.

Soft Cover ISBN: 1-884564-27-5 $22.95

TABLE OF CONTENTS

Introduction

This volume contains a novelized version of the Asarian Resurrection myth that is based on the actual scriptures presented in the Book Asarian Religion (old name –Resurrecting Osiris). This volume is prepared in the form of a screenplay and can be easily adapted to be used as a stage play. Spiritual seeking is a mythic journey that has many emotional highs and lows, ecstasies and depressions, victories and frustrations. The War between Heru and Set is the War of Life that is played out in the myth as the struggle of Heru and Set and those are mythic characters that represent the human Higher and Lower self. How to understand the war and emerge victorious in the journey o life? The ultimate victory and fulfillment can be experienced, which is not changeable or lost in time. The purpose of myth is to convey the wisdom of life through the story of divinities who show the way to overcome the challenges and foibles of life. In this volume the feelings and emotions of the characters of the myth have been highlighted to show the deeply rich texture of the Ancient Egyptian myth. This myth contains deep spiritual teachings and insights into the nature of self, of God and the mysteries of life and the means to discover the true meaning of life and thereby achieve the true purpose of life. To become victorious in the battle of life means to become the King (or Queen) of Egypt.

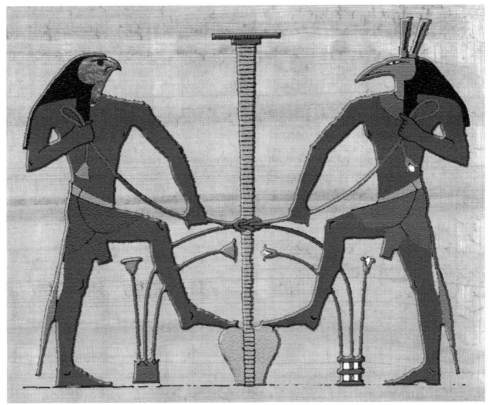

HTP

Peace be with you

Summary of the Asarian Resurrection Myth

The Myth of Asar, Aset and Heru

At the Request of Ra, Asar and Aset incarnated on earth as human beings in order to lead them on the righteous path. They taught farming, religion, righteousness, and vegetarianism. They taught people in Egypt but also around the ancient world.

Asar and Aset dedicated themselves to the welfare of humanity and sought to spread civilization throughout the earth, even as far as India and China.

During the absence of Asar from his kingdom, his brother Set had no opportunity to make innovations in the state because Aset was extremely vigilant in governing the country, and always upon her guard and watchful for any irregularity or unrighteousness.

Upon Asar' return from touring the world and carrying the teachings of wisdom abroad there was merriment and rejoicing throughout the land. However, one day after Asar' return, through his lack of vigilance, he became intoxicated and slept with Set's wife, Nebethet. Nebethet, as a result of the union with Asar, begot Anpu.

Set, who represents the personification of evil forces, plotted in jealousy and anger (the blinding passion that prevents forgiveness) to usurp the throne and conspired to kill Asar. Set secretly got the measurements of Asar and constructed a coffin. Through trickery Set was able to get Asar to "try on" the coffin for size. While Asar was resting in the coffin, Set and his assistants locked it and then dumped it into the Nile river.

The coffin made its way to the coast of Syria where it became embedded in the earth and from it grew a tree with the most pleasant aroma in the form of a DJED or TET. The TET is the symbol of Asar' BACK. It has four horizontal lines in relation to a firmly established, straight column. The DJED column is symbolic of the upper energy centers (chakras) that relate to the levels of consciousness of the spirit within an individual human being.

The King of Syria was out walking and as he passed by the tree, he immediately fell in love with the pleasant aroma, so he had the tree cut down and brought to his palace. Aset (Auset, Ast), Asar' wife, the personification of the life giving, mother force in creation and in all humans, went to Syria in search of Asar. Her search led her to the palace of the Syrian King where she took a job as the nurse of the King's son. Every evening Aset would put the boy into the "fire" to consume his mortal parts, thereby transforming him to immortality. Fire is symbolic of both physical and mental purification. Most importantly, fire implies wisdom, the light of truth, illumination and energy. Aset, by virtue of her qualities, has the power to bestow immortality through the transformative power of her symbolic essence. Aset then told the king that Asar, her husband, is inside the pillar he made from the tree. He graciously gave her the pillar (DJED) and she returned with it to Kamit (Kmt, Egypt).

Upon her return to Kmt Aset went to the papyrus swamps where she lay over Asar' dead body and fanned him with her wings, infusing him with new life. In this manner Aset revived Asar through her power of love and wisdom, and then they united once more. From their union was conceived a son, Heru (Heru), with the assistance of the gods Djehuti and Amon.

One evening, as Set was hunting in the papyrus swamps, he came upon Aset and Asar. In a rage of passion, he dismembered the body of Asar into several pieces and scattered them throughout the land. In this way it is Set, the brute force of our bodily impulses and desires, that "dismembers" our higher intellect. Instead of oneness and unity, we see multiplicity and separateness which give rise to egoistic (selfish) and violent behavior. The Great Mother, Aset, once again sets out to search, now for the pieces of Asar, with the help of Anpu and Nebethet.

After searching all over the world they found all the pieces of Asar' body, except for his phallus which was eaten by a fish. In Eastern Hindu-Tantra mythology, the God Shiva, who is the equivalent of Asar, also lost his phallus in one story. In Ancient Egyptian and Hindu-Tantra mythology, this loss represents seminal retention in order to channel the sexual energy to the higher spiritual centers, thereby transforming it into spiritual energy. Aset, Anpu

6

and Nebethet re-membered the pieces, all except the phallus which was eaten by the fish. Asar thus regained life in the realm of the dead, the Duat.

Heru, therefore, was born from the union of the spirit of Asar and the life giving power of Aset (Creation). Thus, Heru represents the union of spirit and matter and the renewed life of Asar, his rebirth. When Heru became a young man, Asar returned from the realm of the dead and encouraged him to take up arms (vitality, wisdom, courage, strength of will) and establish truth, justice and righteousness in the world by challenging Set, its current ruler.

The Battle of Heru (Heru) and Set

The battle between Heru and Set took many twists, sometimes one seeming to get the upper hand and sometimes the other, yet neither one gaining a clear advantage in order to decisively win. At one point Aset tried to help Heru by catching Set, but due to the pity and compassion she felt towards him she set him free. In a passionate rage Heru cut off her head and went off by himself in a frustrated state. Even Heru is susceptible to passion which leads to performing deeds that one later regrets. Set found Heru and gouged out Heru' eyes. During this time Heru was overpowered by the evil of Set. He became blinded to truth (as signified by the loss of his eyes) and thus, was unable to do battle (act with MAAT) with Set. His power of sight was later restored by Hathor (goddess of passionate love, desire and fierce power), who also represents the left Eye of Ra. She is the fire spitting, destructive power of light which dispels the darkness (blindness) of ignorance.

When the conflict resumed, the two contendants went before the court of the Ennead gods (Company of the nine gods who ruled over creation, headed by Ra). Set, promising to end the fight and restore Heru to the throne, invited Heru to spend the night at his house, but Heru soon found out that Set had evil intentions when he tried to have intercourse with him. The uncontrolled Set also symbolizes unrestricted sexual activity. Juxtaposed against this aspect of Set (uncontrolled sexual potency and desire) is Heru in the form of ithyphallic (erect phallus) MIN, who represents not only the control of sexual desire, but its sublimation as well. Min symbolizes the power which comes from the sublimation of the sexual energy.

Through more treachery and deceit Set attempted to destroy Heru with the help of the Ennead, by tricking them into believing that Heru was not worthy of the throne. Asar sent a letter pleading with the Ennead to do what was correct. Heru, as the son of Asar, should be the rightful heir to the throne. All but two of them (the Ennead) agreed because Heru, they said, was too young to rule. Asar then sent them a second letter (scroll of papyrus with a message) reminding them that even they cannot escape judgment for their deeds; they too will be judged in the end when they have to finally go to the West (abode of the dead).

This signifies that even the gods cannot escape judgment for their deeds. Since all that exists is only a manifestation of the absolute reality which goes beyond time and space, that which is in the realm of time and space (humans, spirits, gods, angels, neters) are all bound by its laws. Following the receipt of Asar' scroll (letter), Heru was crowned King of Egypt. Set accepted the decision and made peace with Heru. All the gods rejoiced. Thus ends the legend of Asar, Aset, and Heru.

The Resurrection of Asar and his reincarnation in the form of Heru is a symbol for the spiritual resurrection which must occur in the life of every human being. In this manner, the story of the Asarian Trinity of Asar-Aset-Heru and the Egyptian Ennead holds hidden teachings, which when understood and properly practiced, will lead to spiritual enlightenment.

The War Heru and Set

An Adaptation of the Book

Asarian Religion (Resurrecting Osiris)
by

Dr. Muata Ashby

P.O. Box 570457
Miami Fl 33257

www.Egyptianyoga.com

© 1998-2005, The King of Egypt/ The War of Life   (305) 378-6253

EXT. DARKNESS OF OUTER SPACE

ON NEBULA

The first view is a dark, watery-like nebula which is
motionless. Suddenly, a ball of golden light begins to emerge
from the depths of the mist. It is a fiery star. In front of
the star is a giant figure. It is a feather of Maat. The
feather is cutting through the mist like a knife and the sun
then follows through it's wake. As the two objects come
closer and pass by, the star becomes brighter and larger and
the feather grows larger as well.

ON THE SUN

The power of the sun clears away the watery nebula as it
moves. As it moves, it disperses the mist and leaves in its
wake planets and galaxies in motion. Now the vastness of
space is visible and the stars and planets are clear.

> TEXT APPEARS ON SCREEN
> This much may be depended
> upon: the religious rites and
> ceremonies of the Ancient Egyptians
> were never instituted upon
> irrational grounds, never built
> upon mere fable and superstition,
> but founded with a view to promote
> the morality and happiness of
> those who were to observe them, or
> at least to preserve the memory of
> some valuable piece of history, or
> to represent to us some of the
> phenomena of nature.
> -Plutarch (c. 46-120 AD)

> DISSOLVE TO:

INT. SHPINX TEMPLE

There is a scribe writing a hieroglyphic text on a wall. As
the camera closes in the text turns into English.

> SCRIBE
> Theses things happened 10,000 years
> ago. This is the story of the
> first king and Queen of Ancient
> Egypt, the gods and goddesses who
> created Egypt and the culture
> which spawned civilization across
> the earth. This is the first story
> of life, passion, pain and the
> struggle to overcome the greatest
> obstacle of life.
>
> This is the first story of the
> struggle between good and evil.

This is the story of the battle
between Heru and Set to be:
THE KING OF EGYPT

                                    DISSOLVE TO:

EXT. PLANET EARTH

ON THE EARTH

As the camera moves closer to one of the planets, the
features of the planet become clearer. It is the earth. As
the camera moves in closer the crystal blue oceans, the brown
land with white scintillating clouds become sharper. The
entire planet is surrounded by a light- glowing aura.

                                    DISSOLVE TO:

EXT. COMING CLOSER TO THE EARTH

 As the camera moves in closer to the earth a hawk flying
high above comes into view.

ON THE EYE OF THE HAWK

The camera separates itself from what the Hawk is viewing and
focuses on the Hawk itself and then the eye of the Hawk,
regal and powerful. The camera moves towards its eye and
takes on the hawks vantage point which is flying in the high
altitude of the atmosphere, surveying all.

ON AFRICA

The Hawk begins to fly over a particular spot on the earth,
it is Africa. It begins to fly in that direction. Then it
moves towards North-East Africa. As it does the Nile river
and the land of Ancient Egypt comes into view.

EXT. AERIAL VIEW OF THE NILE RIVER APPROACHING A PALACE

Flying along the Nile river. In the distance, there is a
great palace. There is a large crowd gathered outside.

INT. CITY OF ABDU, EGYPT 12,000 B.C.-DAY

Moving in through the front doors of the palace The majestic
beauty of the interior, full of colorful paintings and
hieroglyphic art of the palace becomes evident as the
interior hall leading to the interior portion is long.

There is a large crowd gathered inside as well. It is the
throne room of the king of Egypt.

CROWD
(Chanting with
enthusiasm)
Neru Asar! Neru Asar! Neru
Asar! -Victorious Asar-Victorious
Asar!

Moving into the interior of the palace into the throne room.

ON THRONE

Asar (Osiris), the king of Egypt, sits on the throne with his
queen Aset (Isis) and her sister Nebthet (Nephthys) standing
behind him (Aset on the right and Nebethet on the left) with
their arms on his shoulders. Tributes are being brought in
from neighboring lands to honor them.

ASAR
(A young man in his
early 30's, of dark
complexion, sitting
on a throne, smiling
with the distinctive
Atef Crown on his
head)

ASAR
(raising his arms
sitting on the
throne facing the
crowd)

Presently, a king from Asia Minor kneels before them and
presents a scroll at the feet of Asar while looking down (out
of respect). Then he prostrates himself on the floor and the
entire court denotes their approval.

DJEHUTI
(A man with regal
bearing. He wears a
distinctive crown on
his head)
Oh venerable king of the desert
lands, come forth and lift up your
eyes to witness the light of the
world {motioning to Asar}.

KING OF SYRIA
(A middle-aged man
with a noble bearing
with semitic features)
Most learned lord, Djehuti, it is
my honor to behold the threesome
who are the very nature of
goodness and righteousness. I was
so desirous of seeing my lord Asar
once more since he left our land.

Therefore I am overjoyed with the prospect of another visit in this, our time of need. Oh lord of all, I bring you tribute from your devotees in Asia Minor. It is my great honor to be here on the day when our benefactor, the one who brought civilization and religion to our land, the all seeing one, Asar, will celebrate a festivity of thanksgiving to the sun for the wellbeing of the world.

DJEHUTI
Oh gracious lord of Egypt, I now present to you the king of the south, our cousins from Nubia, the golden land.

KING OF NUBIA
(with head bowed)
Hail to you, lord of Abdu, King of kings, benefactor of the world! I offer this tribute of gold and a performance by the renowned dancing girls of our land as a symbol of love and kinship, that our ancient ancestral bonds may never be broken. May the glory of Egypt flow to us as a son's love showers over his parents.

DJEHUTI
And now it is my pleasure to present the king of the eastern lands of India.

KING OF INDIA
Oh great one, pure of heart, bringer of joy and peace, I come to you with gifts of rare spices and fine cloths from the land which is your second home. I greet you as a beloved brother and also hope that our ancestral bonds may strengthen with time.

ASAR
Come forward great sirs, that I may cast my gaze on you who are worthy of your royal crowns, for you have supported the cause of righteousness, peace and justice in your lands with honor and wisdom.

Aset moves closer to Nebethet. Both look almost exactly alike except for their headdress and clothing. The hew of their skin is a dark golden brown.

                    ASET
                (in confidence)
          This is a most joyous day dear
          sister. Today our beloved one is
          being honored by all of the
          neighboring lands where he has
          traveled to instruct people on
          the sciences, arts, agriculture
          and religion.

                    NEBETHET
                (full of enthusiasm)
          Yes sister, I am also filled with
          jubilation at the sight of this
          wondrous procession of nobles.

                    ASAR
                (holding an Ankh
                 scepter and pointing
                 it to those gathered
                 before him)
          All of you have been my followers
          and I could not have accomplished
          such great tasks without your
          help. Therefore, I also salute you
          and bestow blessings upon you all.

                    KING OF NUBIA
                (looking with
                 admiration at Asar)
          Oh, great lord, the entire world
          has been blessed with your very
          presence. Your life has been an
          example and inspiration to all of
          us who seek the righteous path
          which leads to blessedness, peace
          and prosperity. Praises be to the
          Creator, Ra, who sent you to us.
          May you glorify us with your
          blessings for many years to come.

Djehuti looks on with approval but his gaze is drawn to some disturbance which is occurring out of view of the crowd. Because of the location where it is happening, it is a scene that only he can see. Set, the brother of Asar, is looking at the entire scene of the court and turns away in disgust and begins yelling at someone nearby.

ON SET

             SET
         (angrily, to himself)
How long will we have to witness
this disgrace!

          SERVANT (V.O.)
My lord, what do you mean?

            SET
        (turning towards the
        servant)
I am talking about this brother of
mine who is garnishing the
adulation of all peoples. Is there
no end to his charity? Is there no
personal feeling in him. He spends
all of his time planing ways to
establish cities all over the
earth, but does not think of his
own brother.

          SERVANT
But my lord are these things not
good? Should the world not be
civilized and should not the
people of the earth discover the
ways of righteousness and harmony
so as to reap the blessings of
life?

           SET
        (turns to the servant
        angrily, shoving him
        against a wall)
And what do you know of blessings?
Who are you to lecture me on the
virtues of righteous living? I am
the lord of this earth. I was born
only a few days after him, and is
this the reason that he should be
the king while I am the one who
provides strength to this land. I
am Set, Ra has bestowed upon me
the power of nature. I should be
the king.

          SERVANT
Oh lord of the power, indeed you
are the strength of strengths, the
power which engenders desire in
the human heart, but was it not
ordained by your very own
grandfather Ra, that Asar should
be the king and teacher to all
humankind?

15

                    SET
              (turning away and
               looking out a window
               towards the sky)
          Yes you are right. But there is no
          decree that says that I must agree
          with that. I want to enjoy the
          pleasures and wealth of this
          earth. I want to enjoy the
          adulation of the masses and also
          I want what is most precious in
          the world to the king of Egypt.
          Soon the whole of Egypt will know
          of my desires and this most
          hallowed land will place all which
          I desire at my very feet.

As he speaks, Set looks intently at the throne upon which
Asar sits and then he looks at Aset. The camera closes in on
her as she is speaking with her sister Nebethet. The words
they are speaking cannot be heard but the music should be
thematic of Aset.

ON ASET

This view conveys her elegance and beauty. She is humble and
regal, loyal and chaste. But Set looks at her with lust.

It is obvious that he desires her as well as the throne. In
the background, the crowds adulation of Asar can be heard.

ON THE THRONE WITH ASAR, ASET, NEBETHET AND DJEHUTI IN
VIEW

                    CROWD
          Haari Asar! Haari Asar! Haari
          Asar! Haari Asar!

                                        FADE OUT:

INT. NEXT MORNING DAY

Asar and Aset are holding hands as they walk barefoot onto a
balcony which is outside of their bedrooms. Asar dons a white
robe which has ancient symbols decorating the collar, and
Aset wears a see-through robe over a tight fitting gown
underneath which displays the contour of her body.

                    ASAR
          Oh my beloved and dear companion
          of the ages, I cannot take this
          honor alone. You have supported me
          in all of my challenges and you
          have managed this great land in my
          absence. Look my darling, look
          upon the land which we have worked
          so hard for.

16

ASET
(turning to him with
affection)
Sari, my beloved, what is there
left for us now? Have we not
fulfilled the command of our
grandsire, Ra, to civilize this
world and to show the righteous
way of life to men and women? Is
it not time for us to return to
our abode of light to enjoy
eternal peace and tranquility?

ASAR
(turns to Aset with
a loving smile)
For countless eons have you and I
been together.

To this world of time and space we
came from the vast realm of
eternity and to eternity and
infinity will return soon but
there is still an even greater
task ahead which we must fulfill
before returning to our final
rest. There is strife coming in
the future and the prosperity we
have built will be threatened.

Close up - Aset's face becomes filled with concerned.

ASET
Oh dearest one, your words fill me
with foreboding. I feel concern
over what you have said. Tell me,
what is this strife which
threatens the harmony we have
built?

ASAR
In every age there are times of
plenty and times of deprivation.
Our beloved homeland is about to
be struck a blow to the very core
of its foundation, and the true
test of what we have built will
come to pass. It is never possible
to totally stamp out the evil of
anger, hatred and greed in the
human heart. Therefore, order,
justice and harmony, our beloved
Maat, is always being challenged.
Ra in his wisdom created this
challenge so that the soul should
have the opportunity to learn and
grow. This is the way of the

neteru, the forces of nature,
since time immemorial.

       ASET
      (nodding in approval)
You are right of course. Who
better than I know the need to
uphold Maat. The forces of chaos
and disorder are always lurking in
the darkness. I am with you my
lord, to the ends of this earth
and beyond. By our actions, in the
face of adversity, we will teach
others in the most effective way.

       ASAR
      (Asar looks at Aset
      intently)
You have spoken most eloquently,
my dear. It is up to us to show
all humankind the way to achieve
peace and true happiness. By our
actions and by our example we
light the path of knowledge, truth
and self-discovery.

       ASET
O beneficent one, your words fill
me with great peace and trust. May
your words be carried by the four
winds to all corners of the earth.

            FADE OUT:

The camera pulls up and away from the balcony, revealing a
panoramic view of the palace, as the two lovers, holding each
other, peer into the depths of each other souls.

INT. BANQUET ROOM EVENING

Homecoming banquet of Asar. Guests and courtiers donning
characteristic Ancient Egyptian attire from the Pre-dynastic
to the Old Kingdom period - most ancient period- enter the
room. The festivities begin with dancing Nubian girls and
music with traditional Ancient Egyptian musical instruments,
flutes, lute, harp, tambourines and others. Set walks over to
Asar, who is now seated on the throne.

       SET
      (with an evil,
      sarcastic smirk)
Oh gracious brother, you are
receiving the accolades of the
world for your righteous deeds.
May you live long! I would like to
toast in honor of your good works

and the prosperity you have
brought to the world.

          ASAR
          (with a warm smile)
My dear brother, your words of
kindness are pleasing to me. I
accept the honor you are paying me
and wish God's blessings upon you.

Set walks away, having fulfilled his formal duty of honoring
Asar.

          SET
          (As he walks away,
          internally agitated
          and speaking to
          himself)
Yes my brother, I have toasted to
your victory, but only because it
would seem strange to all present
if I had not. I should be the one
receiving the honor since I could
have done twice whatever you have
accomplished!

After the Nubian Dancing Girls perform. Aset, turns to her
sister, Nebethet.

          ASET
          (standing up)
I will retire now sister. There is
much to do tomorrow in preparation
for the festivity. Will you be
coming?

          NEBETHET
Yes sister. I will leave with you.
But internally I would like to
stay all night and share in Asar's
glory.

          ASET
          (with a smile)
You are so proud of him sister.
Sometimes I do not know which one
of us loves him more, you or I!

With a blushing smile, Nebethet turns to Aset and motions her
to go on. Aset now approaches Asar at the throne.

          ASET
          (continuing; with a
          warm smile of
          satisfaction and pride)
Dear one, we will retire now. The
days festivities have been long

and there is much to do now to
prepare for tomorrow's festivity.
Is there anything you need before
I go?

          ASAR
No dearest, you have done so much
already, indeed this honor is not
mine alone, but yours as well. I
will see you later on.

Aset exits the room as the banquet continues.

                              CUT TO:

Set is conferring with some servants in the opposite hallway.
There is a large box. He is giving them instructions and
pointing to it. Then he turns to the hall where the festivity
is taking place and notices that Aset and Nebethet are
leaving.

          SET
          (with anger and
           cunning in his eyes)
Now is the perfect time. The
goddesses are leaving and Asar is
so intoxicated with happiness that
he will not suspect my scheme!

Set turns to his servants and motions to them to bring the
box. Then he moves towards the hall and notices someone
entering there and stops suddenly. It is Lord Djehuti. Set
motions to his servants and they stop and move backwards.
Djehuti enters the room with upraised arms as a sign of
adoration to Asar.

          DJEHUTI
          (with a regal look of
           satisfaction and
           pride approaching
           the throne of Asar)
My dear nephew, I am so proud of
your accomplishments, you have
exceeded the expectations of your
grandfather, Ra, and have
established a new form of culture
which has heretofore never existed
on earth.

          ASAR
You are too kind uncle. You
deserve some credit as well. It
was through your instruction that
I and Aset were able to discover
the mysteries of life and how to
lead others to understand the path

of glory.

It was you who taught us the
wisdom of our most ancient past
and how to meet the challenges of
life through understanding,
righteousness and peace.

>   DJEHUTI
>   (turning to the court)
> Look, oh gracious king. Survey the
> goodness that you have brought to
> the world through your example of
> humility and love. There are
> representatives from all over the
> world here to pay you homage. This
> is a testament to the purity of
> your soul and the goodness of your
> heart.

>   ASAR
>   (with overflowing
>   emotion)
> Oh dearest minister and heavenly
> guide, your blessings have given
> me the opportunity to fulfill the
> highest purpose of life, to
> discover peace. I cannot help but
> want everyone to experience this
> peace and bliss which is
> overflowing in me.

>   DJEHUTI
>   (smiling)
> That is why you have been so
> successful. Your inner peace and
> absence of selfishness is a
> blessing to the earth and all
> nations have recognized this. It
> is to their eternal credit to have
> done so.

Djehuti and Asar turn to look at the crowd.

ON SET ONCE MORE

>   SET
>   (with an angry stare,
>   speaking to himself
>   in disgust,
>   clenching a fist)
> Once again I have been frustrated
> by that mindless uncle of ours!

He is constantly praising Asar and
advising him. I must somehow get

him away from the court so that I
can have time to get rid of Asar.

                                    CUT TO:

INT. ASAR'S CHAMBER LATER THAT EVENING

Asar retires from the party. He reaches his room and goes
straight to the bed and lays down in the dark. After a little
while a figure comes in. It is a dark silhouette and even
seems ominous at first, perhaps even an assassin. Then a part
of the figure comes into the light. It is a female figure.
She makes a sound as she walks through the room which catches
the attention of Asar.

                    ASAR (O.S.)
                 (in a half groggy
                  state)
          Who is there? Is that you my
          dearest?

                    FEMALE UNKNOWN
                 (seductive and
                  voluptuous voice)
          Sari, it is me.

                    ASAR
                 (with trust, opening
                  his arms)
          Come here dearest. Make this
          evening complete with the warmth
          of your embrace.

The figure moves towards the bed and enters into the waiting
embrace of Asar. The two hug each other in the dark with
passion and a light becomes visible between their bodies in
the abdominal area. Their figures are indistinct due to the
darkness.

                                    CUT TO:

EXT. PALACE GARDEN - NIGHT

Lady Aset is walking along a path in the palace garden. She
is looking up at the full moon as she utters words of song.

                    ASET
          "Om Asar, Dua Asar, Om Asar, Dua
          Asar, Nuk meri ta-meri, Nuk meri
          ta-meri, ta Aset meri Asar, ta
          Aset meri Asar" {Hail you divine
          one {Asar}, Hail you divine one
          {Asar}, Adorations to you,
          Adorations to you, I love Egypt,
          I love Egypt, the land where Aset
          is the beloved of Asar, the land
          where Aset is the beloved of Asar}

Lady Aset stands still and the light of the moon shines a ray which engulfs her body. She begins to move as if experiencing some divine ecstasy. She raises her arms and unfurls wings.

                                          CUT TO:

The female figure in Asar's room gets up from the bed and exits the room. Asar remains fast asleep. As the female figure opens the door to the room, she looks first both ways before leaving to make sure that she will not be seen.

One of Set's servants who is out of sight watches as the female figure leaves the room and walks away. He rushes to the room of Set to report what he has seen. The servant reaches the room of Set and knocks on it silently but franticly. Set was sharpening a sword. Set gets up, opens the door and the servant prostrates himself before him.

                    SET
                 (angry)
          What is the meaning of this
          intrusion? Speak quickly or I will
          have you thrown into the pit of a
          thousand cobras this very moment!

                    SERVANT
                 (agitated, facing the
                  ground as he speaks)
          Master, I have seen something. I
          can barely speak of it. You must
          be told, but I fear your wrath!

                    SET
                 (becoming more
                  agitated)
          If you do not speak this very
          moment you will experience the
          hellfire of doom this instant!
          What has caused such turmoil in
          your mind?

                    SERVANT
                 (calming slightly)
          Master, I saw someone leaving the
          room of our king. It was, it was...

                    SET
                 (yelling and grabbing
                  the servant)
          Who did you see leaving his room?

                    SERVANT
                 (looking at Set with
                  foreboding)
          It was a woman of your
          acquaintance, the mistress of the

                            23

earth, the lady of the house.

                    SET
What are you telling me? That Lady
Nebethet entered the room of my
brother for some secret purpose?

                    SERVANT
              (looking down again
               in shame)
Yes my lord. I saw her with my
very eyes not more than a few
moments ago.

                    SET
              (turning away smugly)
What should I care. She has
refused me as her companion and we
have no relations any longer. She
can do as she pleases. Why do you
bring me this news of other
peoples affairs? It does not
concern me. Leave me at once
before I make you regret coming
into my service!

The servant leaves quickly. As soon as he does Set turns
around, his eyes becoming red and his head turning into a
wild beast, with a long aardvark like snout which is his
inner nature.

                    SET
              (continuing; furious
               to himself)
So, dear brother, it is not enough
that you are the master of this
world, but now you propose to take
what Ra has decreed for me, my own
companion! It is not enough that
he has the most beautiful consort
of the universe, Aset, but now he
wants to have two goddesses for
himself? Tomorrow will be a
memorable day indeed. It will be
the day of his end as King of
Egypt. I swear this by the powers
of the universe!

EXT. WISDOM ROOM NEXT MORNING

Lady Aset and Lady Nebethet meet in the Wisdom Room or palace
library. It is a great hall full of papyrus scrolls
containing secret teachings. Aset is reading a scroll as
Nebethet approaches.

                    NEBETHET
              (with a cautious
               smile)
         Greetings dear sister, how was
         your evening communion?

Aset notices something strange on the person of Nebethet.

                    ASET
              (turning around,
               answering with a
               brief hesitation)
         As usual, I bathed in the light of
         the moon and experienced the
         wonders of the night. What is that
         on your neck?

Aset notices a melilot-garland on her neck. Nebethet looks
down on her chest as if surprised.

                    NEBETHET
         Oh this, Asar gave it to me. I
         like it for the pleasant odor.
         Asar has summoned our presence in
         the great hall of thought. Can you
         come now?

                    ASET
              (still staring at the
               garland)
         Oh, oh yes, yes, of course, at
         once. Let me replace this scroll
         and I will walk with you.

Aset replaces the scroll and the two sisters leave the room.
The doors close automatically as they leave.

                                        CUT TO:

INT. HALL OF THOUGHT-DAY

                    ASAR
         My dear brother, to what do I owe
         the visit today?

                    SET
         I have come to pay you homage dear
         brother. Your works have made you
         famous... I came to ask you a
         question. Since you are the ruler
         of this world, by Ra's decree, you
         can surely grant your dear brother
         a favor.

                    ASAR
Speak Set, Speak on. If it is in
my power to give, I will be happy
to do so. Your service to me has
been outstanding and surely you
are worthy of a reward for all you
have done for me and for the
world. You have assisted the
barque of Ra on its journey since
the earliest times. Because of
this he shines in the sky everyday
without interruption and the world
is maintained safe and warm. By
your strength you have enabled me
to do the work which I have
accomplished, therefore, I and
this world are indebted to you for
ever.

                    SET
                (turning to him,
                 agitated)
Yes, yes I have heard this said
many times, and to tell you the
truth, I am tired of guarding Ra's
boat.

I want to enjoy the pleasures of
life, the pleasures of this world!
I do not want to be a servant to
anyone anymore. I no longer wish
to care for the people of this
world.

                    ASAR
                (concerned)
Brother, brother, whence does this
anger come from? I was not aware
of your displeasure.

                    SET
Of course not! You are so busy
tending to the needs of the people
of the earth that you do not know
what is in the heart of your own
brother.

                    ASAR
Brother, brother, what could be
troubling you so? What could you
desire so much that would cause
this anguish?

                    SET
 I demand that you give me the
land of Ethiopia. It is a
bountiful country, our ancestral

26

home. I will be king there and
leave you all to the desires of
your heart. You may serve humanity
until the end of time for all I
care.

                ASAR
            (with compassion)
Dear brother, you know that I
cannot grant you that request. The
land is not mine to give. A king
is appointed by Ra and loved and
supported by the people who he
serves. A kingdom cannot be stolen
or bought. It must be earned by
good works and the trust of the
people who support you. Otherwise,
the people will turn against you
and hate you. They will say that
you are against Maat,
righteousness, order, truth and
justice.

                SET
            (exited and yelling)
I do not care for your lofty
philosophy. All I want is to get
what I deserve! You speak such
high and mighty words, but you do
not follow what you preach.

                ASAR
            (puzzled)
What do you mean by that brother?
If I have committed any error
please point it out to me and I
will soon correct it, lest I be
found guilty of acting against
Maat.

                SET
You know what I am talking about.
It was not enough that you are the
consort of the wisest woman in the
land. Now you have taken another
as well?

                ASAR
            (confused)
What? What is this that you say?
Who is this other?

                SET
Never mind, I expected as much.
You are not even being honest with
me. You are a hypocrite of the
worst kind!

Asar moves towards Set and touches his shoulder.

> ASAR
> Dear brother, whatever the
> problem, is let us talk about it
> and find a solution. Let us
> consult the oracular bull at my
> temple, he will surely provide us
> with answers.

> SET
> (yelling, pushing him
> away)
> Enough! I have spoken of this for
> the last time.

> ASAR
> Brother, please don't leave!

Set storms out of the room and as he exists, he brushes against the Ladies, Aset and Nebethet.

> NEBETHET
> Set, what is the matter, where are
> you going?

Set looks at the two ladies with disdain and walks on hurriedly. The ladies look at each other, wondering about what they have just witnessed. They turn and enter the Hall of Thought where they find Asar with a disappointed look on his face.

> ASET
> Greetings dearest one. Is all well
> with Set? He appeared agitated
> when he left.

> ASAR
> (with a benign look)
> Nothing that patience and
> understanding can not remedy.
> Dearest ones, I have called you
> because there is an important
> matter to discuss. There is a land
> very far away and its leaders have
> requested that I visit them in
> order to teach them the ways of
> civilization and peace. It will be
> a long journey and so I will be
> gone for some time.

Lady Nebethet speaks first, almost blurting out her dissatisfaction.

> NEBETHET
> (agitated)

You have only just returned a few
days ago and you are already
planning another trip. Is it not
possible to send someone else?
Perhaps lord Djehuti can take your
place this time?

      ASAR
       (turning to her with
       a compassionate
       smile)
You know that the special task of
guiding the world has been
entrusted to me by Ra himself.
This is why we have become men and
women.

Would you want me to disobey a
command of the most high God?

      NEBETHET
       (sobbing)
No, no I would not want that. It's
just that we have not had the
pleasure of your company for so
long and now you will leave us
again. It does not seem fair.

Asar turns to Aset for assistance in consoling Nebethet. Aset
moves towards Nebethet and takes her hand.

      ASET
       (with a consoling
       tone)
Dear sister, it is indeed painful
to exist in this world. Sometimes
we are asked to do things which
seem like too big of a sacrifice
or which cause us personal pain,
but this is all the work of Ra. Ra
is the creator of this universe
and everything happens in
accordance with his will for a
higher good. Everything happens
for the good of every life form.
Life's situations are designed to
help us grow so that we may
discover our strength. This is the
purpose of adversity and
sacrifice. Therefore, think about
the good fortunes which we have
and the higher goal to be attained.

      NEBETHET
       (still sobbing, but
       not as hard)
Indeed you are the lady of wisdom.

Even though I feel the sting of
separation, I also feel the wisdom
of your words.

>   ASAR
> Let us not think of pain and
> sorrow today, for I will return
> from the trip as soon as I am
> able. We still have one more day
> of festivity before my departure.
>
> Let us enjoy our time and console
> the people of Egypt who will be
> even more distraught when they
> hear the news of my impending
> departure.

The threesome walk towards the window of the room and look at
the entire city.

>   ASAR
>   (continuing)
> This land of ours has a great
> destiny. One day, people will come
> from all over the earth to study
> the mysteries of life at the feet
> of our Sages. Egypt will show the
> world how the practice of Maat can
> lead to peace and prosperity.
> Therefore, our sacrifice is not in
> vain. It is a testament to our
> love for humanity. Our legacy is
> this most important teaching of
> how to live so as to discover true
> happiness and peace.

>   ASET
>   (with a proud smile)
> You have spoken such beautiful
> words my lord. They are like a
> refreshing breeze on a moonlit
> night. They bring light to a world
> of darkness and direction to the
> lost souls of the earth.

                                        FADE OUT:

EXT. SAILING ON THE NILE AFTERNOON

Asar and Aset take some time away to enjoy the pleasures of
life. There is a cool breeze blowing and the sun shines on
the water, which glistens, producing lustrous, rainbow-like
colors and reflections.

>   ASAR
> Dearest, I have traveled this
> entire world many times and I see

                    30

the hand of the Divine one
everywhere I go. But somehow, this
land, the Nile and its people are
the most special to me.

          ASET
I know what you mean. It is more
than just a homeland. This land is
the first land, the place where
God first stepped, the place where
his words were heard first and his
presence is everywhere to be seen,
in the goodness of the people, the
design of the buildings, but most
of all, in its leaders. There is
no other land where the leaders
are dedicated to righteousness and
truth as the highest goal of life.
My dear, you are the reason for
the special nature of this land,
and this is why the people and I
adore you so.

          ASAR
          (smiling)
Certainly you are mistaken!

          ASET
          (with surprised)
What do you mean?

          ASAR
          (smiling)
How is it possible for the great
lady of wisdom, Aset, the lady of
the words of power, of life and
death, to speak such words of
error?

          ASET
          (with a questioning
          look)
What do you mean? I merely said..

          ASAR
          (cutting her off)
Never mind, never mind. I meant
that you deserve as much credit as
I. How could I go without knowing
there is someone here that I could
trust to take care of our precious
land. You and I are not two
individuals. In reality we are one
and where I am you are also. What
I do, you are also the doer.

          ASET

The Myth of Asar Aset and Heru

>   (moving closer to
>   Asar)
>   May you live long, with health and
>   power, my love. A more loving and
>   considerate husband than you I
>   cannot imagine. I am truly blessed
>   to be in your company. I am
>   forever devoted to you. You are
>   always in my heart.

Aset lays her head on Asar's chest and he hugs her as they
move on in silence. After a few minutes there is a strange
movement on shore. It is a crocodile which is entering the
river as they are passing by. It approaches the small dinghy.
As it approaches, looking ominous, it catches their attention.

>   ASET
>   What is that figure in the water
>   which is approaching us?

>   ASAR
>   I am not sure but I believe it is
>   an old acquaintance we have not
>   seen for some time.

>   ASET
>   Who is that?

Before Asar could answer, the figure emerged from the waters,
beside the dinghy. Now as he emerged from the water it was a
man with some crocodile scales on his body. Upon recognizing
him they both smiled and greeted him.

>   ASAR
>   (joyously)
>   It is Sebek!

Sebek enters the dinghy. In a magical way, water drips from
his body and the parts of his body which enter the boat
become dry as he enters the boat.

>   SEBEK
>   Well, it is nice of you to grace
>   us with your presence. The
>   beautiful Nile is lacking the
>   radiance of its reputation since
>   it does not often see the Lord of
>   the Perfect Black or the Lady of
>   Wisdom any more.

>   ASET
>   My complements Lord Sebek, you
>   know how to make an entrance. You
>   are looking well and your presence
>   has also been missed at the
>   palace. Please tell us, where have
>   you been these past months?

SEBEK

Oh, Lady of Light, your words are soothing to the ear as always. I have been in the land of the south, our ancestral home, in Ethiopia.

ASAR

Tell us great sir, why have you been away for so long?

SEBEK

I was sent there on an important task by your uncle, Lord Djehuti. He asked me to make some inquiries from a certain sage named Ptahotep.

ASAR

This sounds like an important mission if Lord Djehuti himself commissioned it.

SEBEK

Yes indeed. I must now report to you my findings since they concern you and Lady Aset most directly.

ASET

Speak great sir, without delay. The concerned tone in your voice brings foreboding to my mind.

SEBEK

Indeed it does in mine as well. I was told by the great sage Ptahotep that there is a great darkness which will fall over the great black land.

ASET
(insistent)

What is the meaning of this? How can it be possible? Ours is the land of light, the very source of Gods love for the world.

Certainly you are mistaken great sir. There is no possible harm that can befall our land or its people. All of them are blessed with the breath of life from Ra himself. How can there be evil in the heart of any of them? How can there be evil intent in the very earth that sustains us, the sun that warms us or the water which

33

gives life? Where can this danger
possibly come from?

              SEBEK
My lady, my lady. All I know is
that the words of Ptahotep are
true. They were verified by one of
our own great oracles. Lord
Djehuti sent me to verify this
ominous forecast.

Aset looks at Asar for reassurance.

              ASAR
I feel that Lord Sebek's words are
true dearest. Somehow I feel that
a time of great change is coming
for our land. It is true that all
of us have the same divine origin
and our life is sustained by the
one loving Ra. But as you know,
sometimes people forget their own
kinship. They become lost in the
whirlwind of greed and desire for
personal things. When a person
forgets that all life is sacred
and that all human beings are one,
then it is possible that they hurt
nature, others people, or even
commit crimes. This is why Ra sent
us to the world. To teach others
through our example, the way to
overcome ignorance, greed and evil
desires.

              SEBEK
Your words are wise Lord Asar. I
must warn you to be on guard. The
oracle did not say where the
danger would come from but I am
sure it is coming.

              ASET
At once, we will take every
measure to prevent this danger
from coming to us. We will summon
the people and call on the gods
and goddesses of the universe to
protect us and our great land.

Asar turns to Aset with a calming look.

              ASAR
Would that be the righteous thing
to do?

              ASET

How can you say such a thing?
Certainly we must take every
precaution to protect Egypt, our
beloved land, Ta-meri, from any
evil.

ASAR

Dearest, you know as well as I
that good and evil are given to us
by Ra. If some problem is to come,
certainly he has a great plan and
the reasons for the darkness are
justified. If we cause a commotion
because of some danger how can we
teach the people of the earth to
live fearlessly in truth and
peace? We must carry on and only
take the usual precautions. We
cannot live in fear. If we do,
where will the joy of living be?
Ra will protect us and guide us as
he has from the beginning of time.
In any even, adversity is like a
storm, it comes but eventually it
must pass, giving way to
prosperity.

SEBEK

Your faith is commendable, but my
lord, can anyone be trusted when
the source of danger is not known?

ASET
(with resignation and
strength)

Asar speaks wisely lord Sebek.
Everyone's fate is decreed by the
divine plan.

It is compassionate and infallible
and it is always designed to lead
us on the right path. If some
calamity is to befall us, it is
surely directed towards a greater
goal. Therefore, we must accept
fate even as we work to improve
our lives.

SEBEK

Truer and righteous words I have
not heard spoken. Now I know why
you are the king and queen of this
great land. I will remain here now
and I will see Egypt through this
time of trial. If you need me
simply call at the banks of the
river and I will hastily emerge to

35

give assistance.

Sebek turned around and gracefully went over the side of the
dinghy. As he touched the water, the body parts that touched
the water turned into a crocodile. He then disappeared into
the waters of the Nile. Asar and Aset looked into the horizon
and saw the sun setting. They were looking to the future and
determined to meet the challenge ahead.

INT. THRONE ROOM LATER THAT EVENING

The festivities continue. There is a large gathering and the
entire court is present. Set looks on from a balcony and then
turns to one of his servants.

                    SET
               (with a sly look)
          I am holding two scrolls in my
          hand. Give this one to Lady Aset
          and the other to Minister Djehuti
          at once.

                    SERVANT
          Yes my lord, at once.

Set turns to look at the gathering once more.

                    SET
               (to himself)
          Tonight is the night, dear
          brother. I will assume my rightful
          place. Fate can no longer deny my
          right to be the king of Ta-meri.

                                        CUT TO:

The servant walks towards Lord Djehuti and hands him one of
the scrolls, bows and walks away. Djehuti opens the scroll
and looks up to see if the servant is still there but she is
not to be found. Djehuti closes the scroll and walks out of
the throne room. The same servant walks towards Lady Aset.

                    SERVANT #2
          O gracious lady of Wisdom, divine
          queen of the land of light, I have
          a message for you.

                    ASET
          Thank you.

Aset unrolls and reads the scroll and then turns to Lady
Nebethet, who is at her side.

                    ASET
               (continuing; with
               urgency)

Dear sister, we have been summoned
for a meeting in the temple of
reflection. We must leave at once!

      NEBETHET
But sister, what is the reason?
Why is such haste necessary?

      ASET
I will tell you when we arrive
there. This is not the place to
discuss such matters.

The two ladies approach the throne where Asar is seated.

      ASET
        (continuing)
Oh gracious king, we have been
summoned to the temple of
reflection on a matter of great
urgency and we must leave at once.

      ASAR
Is there some problem? Is my
presence required?

      ASET
        (reassuringly)
Your presence is needed here my
lord. Tend to our guests while
sister and I look into this matter.

As the two ladies walk out of the room, Aset turns around for
one more look at Asar at the throne.

Suddenly a feeling of foreboding comes to her. She stops
walking suddenly and the two ladies talk briefly in a
deserted hallway.

      NEBETHET
Sister, what is the heaviness of
heart which I see reflected in
your face?

      ASET
Oh sister, how can I speak of it,
so terrible it is?

      NEBETHET
        (increasingly
         agitated)
What, what is it? Tell me!

      ASET
Just now as I turned to look at
Asar, I was suddenly struck with
the feeling of coldness and

suffering.

               NEBETHET
What could this mean? How can any
calamity befall the throne of
Asar? He is the most exalted ruler
of the earth. His fairness and
wisdom are beloved by all the
world?

               ASET
Sister, I have heard such things
today that make me wonder about
everything. We must hurry to the
temple. Perhaps we will find some
answers there.

The two ladies walk hurriedly to the temple.

               SET
Now that Aset, Nebethet and
Djehuti have left the room there
are no more obstructions to my
plan.

                           CUT TO:

INT. THRONE ROOM -NIGHT

Set is making a grand entrance with several servants. They
are carrying in a marvelous coffin which is covered with gold
and embedded with precious jewels. They approach the throne.

               ASAR
               (pleased)
Dear brother, I was hopping you
would come and celebrate with us.
You have not disappointed me.

               SET
I am hear brother and I have
prepared some entertainment for
your pleasure.

               ASAR
What is this great coffin you have
brought?

Set turns around and addresses the gathered crowd which is
now silent with anticipation.

               SET
Ladies and gentlemen of the court
of our beloved king Asar, and
honored guests from countries far
away, this coffin has been created
by the finest craftsmen of our

country and it will belong to one
of you tonight.

The crowd looks at each other in wonderment at the beautiful
coffin which must be worth a fortune.

        SET
         (continuing)
There is one lucky person in this
crowd whom this precious coffin
belongs to. We will know who that
person is because the coffin will
fit one person and one person
alone perfectly, to the last
measure. So I invite you all to
gather hear and try on this great
coffin. Test your fate and see if
you are the fortunate one tonight!

The crowd gathers around and one by one they get inside the
coffin. Laughing and cheering, one by one they get into the
coffin but to no avail. Finally, there is no one left except
Asar.

        SET
         (continuing)
Well Asar it appears that these
people do not have the right
measurements to fit into this
great container. Try it yourself
and see if the goddess of fortune,
Rennunet herself, is with you tonight!

        ASAR
         (laughing,
          overwhelmed by the
          festive mood)
Yes dear brother, I will certainly
try it on.

As Asar raises himself from the chair, several evil looking
men come closer to the area where the coffin is located from
amongst the crowd. Asar is helped into the coffin by his
brother.

        SET
Well, Well, look at this, a
perfect match! I always said that
my brother was the luckiest man on
earth and here is the proof. Let
us close the lid now to see if the
fit is perfect.

Set closes the lid as Asar, unsuspecting, makes himself
comfortable. With the lid closed completely, Set bends
towards the great coffin and speaks again and deceives the
crowd, making them believe that Asar can hear him. It is so

well sealed that Asar cannot hear anything, nor can anyone outside hear him.

> SET
> (continuing)
> Can you hear me dear brother? Yes
> it is very comfortable isn't it.
> You would like to go now. Very
> well.

Some of Sets servants begin to dance around the coffin while others begin to pick it up. Set turns now to address the crowd.

> SET
> (continuing)
> Ladies and gentlemen, Asar has
> told me that he wishes to exit in
> grand style.
>
> He will see you again after he
> returns from his trip around the
> world.

Set's servants begin a procession out of the great room. The festivities continued since everyone thought that this was all staged for their amusement by Set and Asar. Some even congratulated Asar as a magnificent host. As they leave the room. Set turns to one of his servants.

> SET
> (continuing; in
> confidence)
> Follow the plan as we arranged
> earlier, meet me at the banks of
> the Nile river, at the spot I
> showed you and do not tell anyone
> where you are going.

The servant leaves without saying a word. Set turns to the crowd and smiles to himself.

> SET
> (continuing)
> Not yours to give, well if you
> will not give, then I will just
> have to take what is mine. That is
> the law that I live by. I am the
> stronger and I can have whatever
> I want. Only those who are
> ruthless and conning are worthy to
> rule the earth. Therefore, I will
> live the good life while you sink
> to the bottom of the river.

> CUT TO:

INT. TEMPLE OF REFLECTION

Aset and Nebethet arrive at the temple. They see a figure
seated in a cross-legged posture in front of an altar. On the
altar is the symbol of the crescent moon. The figure turns
towards the entranceway to see who is coming. The two ladies
stop and for a moment they seem to see an ibis bird-like
figure but as they slowly come closer they realize that it is
Lord Djehuti.

                    NEBETHET
                (agitated)
          Lord Djehuti, why have you
          summoned us here on such short
          notice?

          What is the reason for the
          disquieting note we received,
          saying that our presence here is
          important to the survival of the
          nation?

                    DJEHUTI
          Calm, calm my dearest niece, there
          is no need to worry.

                    ASET
                (insistent)
          No need to worry? Dear sir please
          explain to us what is happening.
          Why have you summoned us here?

                    DJEHUTI
          I did not summon you hear. I
          myself was summoned. I received a
          note asking that I should come
          here at once. I arrived a few
          moments before you and found no
          one so I decided to meditate a
          while on that which is before us.

                    ASET
                (determined)
          But if you did not summon us who
          did? What is the meaning of this?

                    DJEHUTI
          I am certain that whoever summoned
          us had a reason for doing so. I am
          certain that this reason will be
          revealed very soon. Sit with me a
          while.

                    ASET
          Dear uncle, many strange things
          have happened today. If you only

41

knew of the bizarre feelings I
have had lately, you would not ask
me to sit at a time like this.

    DJEHUTI
My dear child, it is indeed
because I know of these things
that I ask you to do this. From
time immemorial I have been your
guide and matters of state, in
matters of the heart and matters
of the soul. Have you ever had
cause to doubt me?

    ASET
     (calming down,
      looking at Nebethet)
Well, of course not.

    DJEHUTI
Then sit with me and the answers
you seek will be revealed to you.

The two ladies sit next to Lord Djehuti. After a few moments
in silence, the three of them appear in a paradisiacal
setting. It is a heavenly place, and they are amongst the
clouds observing the horizon.

    NEBETHET
What is this place? Why have we
come here?

    DJEHUTI
Watch in the distance.

    ASET
It is Grandfather, look it is Ra
in his beautiful radiance.

The morning sun is rising over the horizon, within it is a
figure of a scarab-beetle. As it approaches, the image inside
the sun turns into a man of 60 years of age.

    NEBETHET
     (with joy)
Adorations! Look, it is Ra taking
his usual journey across the
heavens to illuminate and bring
life to the world.

    ASET
Yes, yes... It is as if I have
seen this exact time and place
before. It is like a memory that
I had forgotten.

DJEHUTI
Yes my dear. Look and you will
understand.

The threesome are now onlookers, observers of the scene of
the rising sun. They are witnessing the scene as if from a
distance, a scene which occurred long ago. They see the
figure of Aset approaching Ra as he comes closer.

ASET
(with upraised arms
towards Ra)
Grandfather, grandfather, it is my
special joy to see you in your
greatest glory once again. There
can be no other radiance as
lustrous as yours. You are the
light of all lights, the source of
all Creation. Adorations to you a
thousand times!

Aset prostrates herself before Ra and touches his feet.

RA
Dearest granddaughter of mine, you
are the very reflection of me as
a mirror reflects an image. You
have come to greet me every
morning to receive my light and
you have thereby become the
renowned lady of wisdom and truth.

ASET
Oh grandfather, exalted one among
the exalted, I have become wise
indeed but only in matters of
worldly things. I know all there
is to know about the sciences, the
words of power which control
nature and the human heart, but I
am devoid of true knowledge just
the same. I am destitute in my
wisdom. I know nothing even though
I know all about life on earth.

RA
Dearest one, why do you feel that
you have nothing when you have
accomplished so much?

ASET
Because I have discovered that all
worldly knowledge is perishable,
just as the earth is perishable
and will some day come to an end.
Therefore, it is limited and

43

imperfect. Even the gods and
goddesses, who live for thousands
of years will some day come to an
end! Even the great pyramids will
crumble into dust one day.

Everything is perishable, this
lesson I have learned from the
world well. Is there nothing more
beyond this? I want to know. I
need to know the purpose of my
existence and the place from which
all comes.

Ra turns away and looks in the distance for a moment. He then
turns towards Aset.

                    RA
          Dearest granddaughter, you have
          devoted yourself to my worship, as
          your faithful visitations to my
          risings attests. You have earned
          the boon of knowledge and I will
          impart to you the knowledge which
          you seek. Ask on and receive that
          which you value so highly.

Aset and Nebethet, who are looking on, turn to each other.

                    NEBETHET
          Dear sister is this a fantasy or
          did it occur long ago in the past?

                    ASET
          I recall this day now as if it
          were just yesterday. It is strange
          indeed that I would have forgotten
          such a remarkable day. Somehow it
          is as if I never forgot. The
          feeling was always there but I
          never understood where it came
          from.

The two ladies turn to Djehuti, who is looking at them with
a soft smile. He then turns back to the scene and so do the
two ladies.

ASET
(continuing)
All of my knowledge is about
things that fade in time. I know
how to create a palace by merely
uttering certain special words. I
can heal a broken leg or cause a
plant to bring forth fruit even
out of season. I can create rain
or a stormy wind by a mere willing.

These power I have gained from my
knowledge but none of these things
lasts. The person with the broken
bone with cease to exist some day,
the temples will all become ruins
and all life on earth will come to
an end at the time of dissolution,
when you will dissolve this
Creation and create a new
universe. Therefore, what is the
use of this world? What is the
purpose of having knowledge of
things that are perishable in the
end? I want to know that which is
eternal, transcendental and pure.
I want to understand that which is
beyond understanding. I want to
know what lies beyond this
fleeting mortal existence. My
knowledge leads me to believe that
you are the greatest mystery. You
sustain Creation and yet no one
knows you.

RA
(chuckling)
Oh my dear, you are mistaken.
Everyone knows me. I am the
morning sun in my form as the
great beetle. At noontime I am the
sustainer of the day in the form
which you see now. At dusk I am
the old and gray sun in my name as
Tem, the closer of the day. I am
the sustainer of Creation and I
hold every atom of creation in my
hand. What more is there to know?

ASET
All of these things that you just
said I know well. But what happens
to Creation at the end of time?
How does the universe dissolve
into a watery mass leaving no more

46

earth or stars? What happens to
the soul when a person dies?
Whence have you come from and what
is your nature, that you are
eternal and transcendent of all
these things? Might I share in
this wisdom so that I too may
become eternal and immortal?

            RA
Dearest granddaughter, few are the
souls which come to me as you
have, asking such questions about
life. Many are the men and women
who are satisfied with the
knowledge of the world and few
seek after that which is
transcendental and eternal.
Therefore, you are exalted among
all women and men because you seek
after the highest truth. If you
would know this highest of all
forms of knowledge you cannot do
so as you are.

            ASET
What do you mean, What must I do?

            RA
Beyond all things of Creation am
I. I am the highest knowledge
since I am the source and
sustainer of all forms of
knowledge and science. The
knowledge which you seek cannot be
told by speech or found in books.
In order for you to understand you
must go beyond yourself. Leave
behind all that you have learned
and come into my very heart. This
is the only way.

            ASET
How can I do that?

            RA
Think of me only and forget all
else, even yourself, and you will
find the way to my heart.

Ra and Aset close their eyes and suddenly, Ra becomes a mass
of light energy and then Aset walks into the mass and
disappears. After a few moments the scene fades into a mist
and then only clouds are visible. Nebethet, watching from a
distance in amazement turns to Djehuti for counsel.

            NEBETHET

The Myth of Asar Aset and Heru

Adorations to the most high one!
Tell us uncle, what have we just
observed? What is the meaning of
this beautiful scene?

          DJEHUTI
          (turning towards them
           with reverence)
Dearest one, ask your sister, who
is beside you.

          ASET
          (captivated by the
           scene)
I..., I remember, I remember. Ra
imparted to me the knowledge of
his very essence.

          NEBETHET
What is his essence?

          ASET
My very self.

          NEBETHET
          (in disbelief)
What do you mean sister, you are
not Ra are you?

          ASET
It is true. When I communed with
Ra I saw my self. Not my self as
the goddess but my universal self.
I saw that all of us are one in
Ra. We all come from the same
source and we are kin to each
other, not by blood but by the
very essence of our existence. All
life in the universe is one. All
people are one!

          NEBETHET
What else did you discover, sister?

          ASET
Ra imparted to me the power which
only he has, the power to bring
life. There is one more thing
sister, I remember now that Ra
told me I would come to the earth
with a twin sister, who is not my
twin.

          NEBETHET
          (continuing)
What do you mean, am I not that
very same twin?

48

                    ASET
No you are not.

Nebethet stares in disbelief.

                    ASET
                (continuing)
This will be difficult sister but
you must hear it now. You are not
my sister, but a reflection of my
very self. Have you ever wondered
why we are opposite in everything,
our dress, our crown, our
interests? I seek knowledge while
you always liked earthly things.

                    NEBETHET
Yes, yes, I have wondered about
that from time to time, but can
this be really true?

                    ASET
We are opposites in all things
except one, our love and devotion
to Asar. We are two manifestations
of the same soul. This is our
great strength and it will also be
the source of our greatest trial.
You and I have a great destiny to
fulfill. We will have a great
struggle against evil in our time.
What we will do, no women have
ever done before. We will show the
way of honor, peace, love and
devotion for all future
generations to follow.

                    DJEHUTI
Aset speaks the truth, I have
heard Ra speak of this many times.

                    ASET
But uncle, why have you never
mentioned this to me?

                    DJEHUTI
Dearest one, for all things there
is a time and your time has come
to remember who you are, for the
task that awaits you will be
arduous and traitorous. You will
both need the strength and power
of the highest wisdom in order to
succeed in the coming struggle.

As Djehuti concluded his last word, they all opened their

eyes and found themselves sitting in the Temple of Reflection once again.

> DJEHUTI
> (continuing)
> You must leave now. And prepare
> yourselves for the great task
> ahead.

Djehuti fell silent and closed his eyes. The two ladies, realized that he would speak no more. They left the meditation room and headed back to the throne room.

EXT. THE BANKS OF THE NILE EVENING

Set arrives at the appointed location where he was to meet his servants with the coffin.

> SET
> You have all served me well. Now
> follow my instructions so that we
> may get rid of this fool king who
> is inside the box.

One of the servants walks up to Set.

> SERVANT
> Lord Set, how is it that there is
> no noise in the coffin?

> SET
> I cleverly placed a sleeping
> potion inside so that anyone
> staying in too long would fall
> asleep and never know what had
> happened. Let us not delay any
> longer, the new king wants to get
> back to the palace. Throw the
> coffin into the Nile and let it
> sink and never be seen again.
> Nobody can help you now Asar! Join
> the god of the river, and may you
> never be seen again!

With one big heave the servants toss the coffin into the Nile. At first it seems to sink by then floats away into the darkness. Unbeknown to Set and the servants there was someone holding the chest up so that it would not sink. It was the god Happi. The servants walk away from the shore to the place where Set was standing. Suddenly they become afraid at the sight of a figure they cannot recognize and which seems to look ominous.

> SERVANT
> Who is there, speak to us who are
> the servants of Lord Set.

The Myth of Asar Aset and Heru

The figure comes into the light. It is Set in his wrathful
form. The servants gradually step backwards in fear.

                    SET
          Come closer, loyal servants of
          mine. Come and receive your reward
          for your service.

Set turned into a beast and began to kill the servants one by
one. Unbeknown to Set, one of the servants had brought along
his two young sons-ages ten and eight- who had been walking
along the banks of the river a ways down stream. When they
heard the commotion they returned to the place where they had
left their father. Seeing Set in a rage they hid behind some
tall papyrus plants which jutted out of the riverbanks. They
watched the scene in horror as their father was being killed.
The last servant turns to Set before receiving the final
blows that will end his life.

                    SERVANT
               (in pain and sobbing)
          Why do you kill us master? We have
          been your loyal and devoted
          servants. Why do you repay us in
          this ruthless manner?

                    SET
          Yes you are loyal and devoted. Now
          you will devotedly keep the secret
          of what happened here and take it
          with you to the next life!

As Set pounces on the servant for one last fatal blow the
CAMERA goes black as he engulfs his victim.

                              FADE OUT:

INT. THRONE ROOM NIGHT

Lady Aset and Lady Nebethet reach the throne room but find
that everyone has already left for the evening. So they sit
in the empty room and talk for a while.

                    NEBETHET
          Aset, dear sister, tonight I have
          discovered a closeness with you
          that I never knew existed. And yet
          somehow it is as if I always knew.
          Do you understand?

                    ASET
          Yes, I share the same feeling. I
          also understand why you have
          turned away from Set in favor of
          Asar. If your feeling for Asar is
          as mine, then it is pure and good.

51

How can such a love be given to
one who is egoistic and cruel?

                    NEBETHET
You speak of Set?

                    ASET
Yes.

                    NEBETHET
Set is egoistic, he seeks to
please only himself and all but I
never thought of him as cruel.

                    ASET
I don't know why but whenever I
see him it is as if he is trying
to consume me, as he tries to
satisfy his insatiable desires for
worldly objects and pleasures.

                    NEBETHET
You know, it is as if I have had
the same feeling but was unable to
express it.

Lets us go dearest. We must prepare for Asar's trip tomorrow.

                                        FADE OUT:

EXT. NILE RIVER DELTA NEXT MORNING

The coffin carrying the body of Asar has floated out of Egypt
and has come ashore on the banks of the river in the land of
Syria. The god Happi hauled it out of the water and placed it
on the shore.

                    HAPPI
                 (sorrowful)
Oh my lord, what has happened to
you? What will be the fate of this
world without you? I, the god
Happi, the protector and nourisher
of the Nile river bow to you in
homage. I hope that you will
receive here a peace that you did
not find in our land.

Happi turned around and walked into the water and
disappeared. Happi left the coffin in a horizontal position
but it moved itself to a vertical position. In that place the
coffin became embedded in the ground and in a few hours-SHOW
BY TIME LAPSE- a tree grew around it. The tree became
luscious and full of fruits. Two passersby, the king of Syria
and a servant, notice the tree.

                    SERVANT

Look at that, Sire, I was here
just yesterday and did not notice
the beautiful tree. What kind of
tree is it?

                    KING OF SYRIA
You are right, let us investigate
this miracle.

They approach the tree and marvel at its size and pleasant
aroma.

                    KING OF SYRIA
                 (continuing; taking
                  a deep breath)
Do you smell that. With every
breath I take I feel a peace that
I cannot understand. Its pleasant
aroma is a wonder indeed. With
every breath I feel transported to
a place of overflowing greenery
and life. Summon my palace
architect at once. I will have
this magnificent tree cut down and
made into a pillar for my palace.
In that manner I will enjoy the
beauty and fragrance of this tree
for the rest of my days.

                                    FADE OUT:

EXT. CITY LIMITS NEXT MORNING

Aset and Nebethet arrive at the borders of the city of Abdu.
There is no one there except a farmer tilling the soil. Aset
walks up to him.

                    ASET
Gracious sir, could you help me?

                    FARMER
                 (prostrating himself
                  before her)
Oh great lady of wisdom, today I
am truly blessed. I never thought
I would ever have the good fortune
to see the lady of truth! You have
truly blessed me today. The mere
sight of you is the source of
courage and determination. How can
I serve you my lady? Ask and it
will be my command!

                    ASET
Please rise noble sir, your
recognition of me is pleasing to
my heart. You will have the best
crop this year and your altar will

never lack incense and the
materials necessary to perform the
rituals of worship. Tell me, where
is everyone? We expected to see a
great procession today, since Asar
was to leave the city on a special
trip.

                    FARMER
I have seen no one this morning
until your arrival great lady.
perhaps the procession took a
different rout.

                    ASET
No, that was not possible, this
western end of the city is the
prescribed rout for leaving the
city because it brings auspicious
energies to the traveler. Thank
you noble sir, blessings be to you
and your family.

                    FARMER
Adorations to you my lady.

The farmer walks away towards the plough and Aset returns to
the place where Nebethet is standing.

                    NEBETHET
Sister, where is everyone?

                    ASET
The noble farmer has told me that
he has seen no procession this
morning.

                    NEBETHET
Where is Asar then? He was not in
his quarters or anywhere in the
palace.

                    ASET
Let us return to the palace and
inquire more deeply.

                                        CUT TO:

INT. ASAR'S ROOM DAY

The ladies return to the palace and go to Asar's room. They
find a servant there but it is a strange person they have not
seen before. The servant is looking for something.

                    NEBETHET
Who are you and what are you doing
here?

                    SERVANT
               (surprised)
          I, I, nothing my lady. I was
          merely cleaning before our lord
          returns.

                    NEBETHET
          Where is Lord Asar?

                    SERVANT
          The palace staff was told that he
          had left early this morning for
          his journey of peace around the
          world.

                    NEBETHET
          Who told you this?

                    SERVANT
          Lord Set my lady.

                    NEBETHET
          Where is Lord Set now?

                    SERVANT
          I was told that he went out to
          hunt for boars as it is his custom
          my lady.

                    NEBETHET
          You may leave now.

                    SERVANT
          Yes my lady.

                    NEBETHET
          Sister, what is going on? I feel
          that something is not right. I
          fear for the safety of Asar. He
          would never leave without saying
          good-bye.

                    ASET
          I too feel a strange vibration in
          the air. Let us seek out Lord
          Djehuti. Surely he will know what
          has happened.

As they turned to leave the room they head a strange noise in
the next room adjacent to that one.

                    ASET
               (continuing)
          Did you hear that sister?

                    NEBETHET
          Yes, let us investigate.

Aset opens the door slowly and they enter the room. It was
the manservant of Asar. He was wounded but still breathing.
They rushed to his side.

                    ASET
               (alarmed)
          What has happened? Who did this to
          you? Where is Asar?
                    MANSERVANT
               (gasping)
          Asar is...cough, cough.

                    NEBETHET
          Sister, can you do anything for
          him. Can you use your power to
          restore his life?

                    ASET
          No I cannot. He has met his fate
          in accordance with the karmic laws
          of Maat. If I interfere I will
          bring disharmony in the universe.
          He is beyond help now but we can
          make him comfortable in his last
          moments before he goes to the hall
          of judgement in the next life.

                    NEBETHET
               (turning to the
                manservant with
                compassion)
          Oh noble one, you have fulfilled
          your duty on this earth. You will
          soon go to the next life. Tell us
          now with your last breath, what
          has happened here.

                    MANSERVANT
               (gasping)
          I was putting things in order in
          my master's room, when several men
          came from behind me. Without
          saying a word they stabbed me and
          laughed. I heard one of them say
          that Asar will suffer the same
          fate. I fear he is dead.

Upon hearing this Aset immediately felt foreboding in her
heart. A most serious look fell on her face. Nebethet was
shocked in disbelief. The manservant took a last breath and
expired.

                    NEBETHET
               (agitated)

What, what is the meaning of this?
How is it that violence has come
to our peaceful palace? How could
this be?

          ASET
          (agitated; with
           sorrow)
Asar is gone from us. My beloved
lord is no longer on this earth.

          NEBETHET
          (sobbing)
No, no sister don't say that
horrible thing, no.

          ASET
I can feel it.

The two ladies sat there sobbing beside the dead manservant.
Nebethet was more intensely affected. She could not control
her sorrow. After a few moments, Aset stood up and walked to
the bathroom chamber and came out, silently but internally in
grief, with a knife.

          NEBETHET
          (still sobbing)
Sister, what are you doing?

Without answering, Aset took the knife in her right hand and
grabbed a lock of hair in her left hand. She immediately
proceeded to cut off the lock and dropped it on the ground.
Then she dropped the knife. The two remained in silence for
a while.

          ASET
          (in pain but
           internally resigned
           to what had happened)
Come sister, let us find the body
of our loved one. Let us bring it
back to our temple so that it may
receive a proper resting place.

                              FADE OUT:

EXT. CITY STREET DAY

The two ladies went out into the city to see if they could
find anyone that knew what had happened to Asar. As the day
wore on they became increasingly frustrated at not finding
even a clue as to Asar's whereabouts.

          NEBETHET
Where should we go next sister? We
have searched everywhere in the
city and have found nothing.

                    ASET
          If there is nothing in the city
          then we will have to leave the
          city and search the countryside.

So they left the city and came to the river banks and sat
down to rest.

                    NEBETHET
          Sister, do you think we will ever
          find out what happened to Asar?

                    ASET
          Surely, we will. As surely as Ra
          traverses the sky everyday without
          fail, so too we will search with
          diligence and our efforts will be
          successful. I know it is hard
          sister, but this is the most
          important task of our life. It is
          the reason for which we were born.

                    NEBETHET
               (drawing strength
                from Aset)
          I feel your passion and I am
          confident in your words. Let us
          rest a while and then resume the
          search.

The two ladies lay to rest along the riverbanks at the base
of a beautiful palm tree which afforded them shade. Suddenly
they heard the voices of some children which were coming
towards them. The voices were upset. They were crying and
shocked.

                    SON #1 OF SET'S SERVANT
               (upset and crying)
          What will we do? What will we do?
          We are all alone, how will we
          survive without father? Where will
          we go?

                    SON #2 OF SET'S SERVANT
               (sobbing)
          I don't know. I don't know. I am
          afraid for our lives. Maybe the
          evil one will come after us too.

Aset walks up to the children.

                    ASET
          Why are the young children from
          this black land crying? What
          calamity has befallen you on this

day to cause such sorrow and pain?

The children stop and begin to stare at the magnificent lady.
They don't know if they should speak or keep silent.

                    ASET
                    (continuing)
          Come closer my dears, do you not
          know who I am? I am Lady Aset, the
          great queen of this land. I am the
          lady of wisdom. You can trust me
          to help you in your problem.

After a few moments one of the children speaks.

                    SON #1 OF SET'S SERVANT
          I am the eldest son of my father
          but he is now gone to the next
          life. You cannot help me or my
          brother. We will leave this land
          of horror. Leave us alone.

                    ASET
                    (with a compassionate
                    chuckle)
          Where will you go, and how will
          you survive? You are too young to
          work and too skinny to make the
          journey to the next city. It
          appears that you are cold and
          hungry even now.

Aset moves closer to the children who are holding each other
in fear. She crouches to their level. As she comes closer to
them she begins to manifest a golden aura which captivates
the attention of the boys. She embraces them and at once they
reciprocate by hugging her and then they call out to her.

          SON #1 OF SET'S SERVANT   SON #2 OF SET'S
SERVANT

          Maa, Maa Save us! Save us   Maa, help us, please.
          from the evil one. He will
          surely kill us.

                    ASET
                    (with a motherly
                    (smile
          Yes, yes, of course I will take
          care of you. Have no fear. Now
          tell me why you are so frightened
          and what happened to your father?

                    SON #1 OF SET'S SERVANT
                    (looking down)
          Father was killed last night and
          since then brother and I have
          wandered in the papyrus swamps.

ASET

Who did this horrible thing? What
happened? Tell me at once.

          SON #1 OF SET'S SERVANT
His name is Lord Set. My father
was his servant and he along with
other servants, brought a great
coffin to the banks of the Nile.
Then they threw it into the
river.
Then brother and I heard a great
noise. We ran to the place where
father was and then...

          ASET
Yes, and then what happened?

          SON #1 OF SET'S SERVANT
          (sobbing)
Then Lord Set killed him and
later
laughed. He said "Now I have
gotten rid of the king and now I
am the king. He also said that
Aset will now be my queen or she
will meet the same fate as her
husband.

On hearing these words Aset stood up and she knew she would
not be able to return to the city.

          ASET
We can no longer return to the
city. Come children, we will go to
a safe place where you will be
taken care of from this day forth.

They walked over to the place where Nebethet was. As they
walked, Aset noticed a dinghy tied to the shore. As they
approached they saw the lady stretched out on the ground. She
was asleep and a strange luminescence was emanating from her
abdominal area. Aset paused for a moment and suspected what
the meaning of the light was.

          ASET
Sister, sister wake up!

          NEBETHET
          (groggy)
Yes, sister, is it time to go
now?

          ASET
Yes we must leave at once. These
children have informed me as to
the fate of Asar. We must leave

61

here at once and see to their
safety and then continue the
search. There is a dinghy nearby.
We will use it to go to my
temple.
We will be safe there for this
night.

They all get into the dinghy. Aset paddls the small vessel
on its way. Nebethet begins to experience some discomfort.

                    NEBETHET
                (holding her abdomen)
        Sister, I feel a strangeness
        stirring within me. Can we rest
        some place to relieve my illness?

                    ASET
        It is no illness what you have
        dearest one. Soon you will be
        relieved from this burden. We
        will
        reach the temple soon.

                                        CUT TO:

EXT. TEMPLE OF ASET DUSK

They soon reach a magnificent temple on an island in the
middle of the Nile River. They disembark and walk up to the
entrance. Aset knocks at the great entranceway door.

                    PRIESTESS
        In the name of Rekhat, the
        goddessof wisdom and peace, who is there
        and what is your business?

                    ASET
        It is Aset the queen of the black
        land and wife of the lord of the
        perfect black. Open with haste,
        for a darkness has fallen upon
        the black land and her people are in
        fear.

                    PRIESTESS
                (opening the door
                 with haste)
        Oh what a glorious day this is,
        the very same lady who is the
        object of my worship is here.
        Come, come in please!

The priestess of the temple prostrates herself at the feet
of
Aset.

                    ASET
                (raising her
Blessings be to you, loyal one.
Come, come, there is little time
and there is an arduous task
ahead. Take Lady Nebethet to the
Meskhenet chamber at once. Make
her
comfortable and prepare for
the coming of a new soul into our
world.

The priestess and some other attendants help Lady Nebethet
away and then Aset motions other priestesses to take the
children.

INT. INNER SHRINE-TEMPLE OF ASET

Aset walks into the inner shrine of the temple and sits on
her knees and heels with upraised arms in front of an altar
with a large painting in the background of two figures, a
dark skinned male and a dark skinned female. The male figure
is lying on the ground on his back facing upwards, the
female
figure is above him stretching herself over him from end to
end.

                    ASET
                (bowing with eyes
                 closed)
Adorations to you Geb, Adorations
to you Nut, the divine ones who
gave birth to me. The calamity of
these days has brought me here and
I seek your help now more than
ever. I am faced with a formidable
task and I do not know if I can
meet the challenge. Please help
me. My husband has been murdered
and lost and not I will be the
next victim of the murderer if I
cannot succeed in finding Asar and
bringing him back to life so that
he can take his rightful place as
king again.

Aset pauses, rests her arms on her thighs and closes her
eyes.

                    ASET
I know what will happen if Set
succeeds in taking the throne, our
land will suffer the burden of his
insatiable desires and cruel ego.
Right now before me is a pressing
task though. Lady Nebethet is with

child and I know who the father
is. It was Asar! Sister had a
melilot garland which Asar
reserved for me alone. It was an
unlawful union and now I am called
upon to act as midwife to bring
this child into the world. But how
can I do this? How could sister
have betrayed me in this way?

There is a moment of silence. Then the ground begins to
tremble and thunder and lightning can be heard from above.
Aset opens her eyes and to her left she sees a smoky figure
emerging from the ground. It takes human form as a man. On
her right a female figure descends from the ceiling. The
man's body is encrusted with the elements and minerals of
the earth. He dons an ethereal garment of light. The woman was
radiant, as if she had small stars embedded in her lustrous
sable colored skin. She also dons an ethereal garment of
light.

        ASET
      (prostrating herself
      at their feet)
Oh divine father, god of the
earth. Mother dear, the mistress
of the heavens, adorations to you
both. You grace me here at the
time of my greatest need.
Adorations to you both.

        GEB
What is this I have heard you
say,
fearless daughter mine, that you
do not want to help your sister?

        NUT
Oh, divine lady of love and life,
how can it be that you are in
such a state of uncertainty?

        ASET
My heart tells me that I must
Help her in every way but my mind
tells me to be angry and spiteful. I am
torn between the two and do not
know how to proceed. Please guide
me.

        NUT
Who are you?

        ASET
What? I am Aset of course, your
daughter.

              GEB
No, who ARE you?

            ASET
I do not understand. Please,
please help me to understand.

              GEB
         (turning to Nut)
Has the lady of wisdom suddenly
forgotten who she is? Has she
forgotten her great meeting with
Ra, the exalted one? None of the
gods and goddesses have
experienced what Aset has. Has she
forgotten the glory of what she
knows?

             NUT
Remember daughter, remember what
you learned in your communion
with Ra and you will know the path you
must follow.

The two figures dissolve into a mist and disappear.

            ASET
No wait, please. Don't leave me.

             NUT
        (in a soothing
        ethereal voice)
We will never leave you dearest.
We are as close as the earth and
the heavens and always watching
over you. Seek the knowledge
which
you possess and you will know the
right path...

            ASET
        (to herself)
Seek the knowledge which I
possess... Seek the knowledge
which I possess... Lord Djehuti
was wise in guiding me to the
vision of Ra. But there is
something more that I need to
know. What happened when I walked
into the light of Ra?

Aset closes her eyes and recalls the events in her mind's
eye. She is walking into the light as she saw earlier. Once
inside it the light expanded to encompass all things. She
saw the past, the times with Asar and vast universes and vast
worlds being created and destroyed in an ongoing cycle.

The Myth of Asar Aset and Heru

ASET
Ra, Ra where are you?

Ra approaches seemingly out of nowhere.

ASET
Oh divine one, you have shown me
the wonders which no man or woman
or god or goddess has ever seen.
you have created and destroyed
countless worlds for all
eternity.
There is no greatness which
surpasses yours. Adorations to
you!

RA
Aset, there is something yet
lacking in your knowledge. Without
it, all the wonders you have
learned here today will not be
enough to satisfy the craving in
your innermost heart.

ASET
Please instruct me great sire of
universes. Let there be nothing
left unknown, unsaid or undone in
my enlightenment. Make of me that
which is like unto perfection so
that there will never again be
lacking in my understanding or my
heart ever again.

Ra transforms himself from a human form to a human body with
the head of a hawk. His voice is now ethereal.

RA
Perfection cannot come from
wonders or sciences or knowledge.
It comes from being and there is
no other being except my being. I
am the mover behind all universes.
I am the sustainer of the energy
in the smallest atoms. I am the
source of life which dwells in the
egg of a bird and I am the love
which burns in the heart of all
living beings. Every form of life
is within me and I am within them.
Without me they cannot exist. Life
itself cannot exist. The universe
cannot exist. I am time itself,
without me time and space dissolve
into the primeval soup before
Creation comes into being. You

66

asked me once to tell you your
purpose and the source from which
you come. You will know the former
when you learn the latter.
Therefore, follow me now into
eternity. Follow me know to the
infinite realms of existence.

Aset moves towards Ra. Before them is a tunnel of light.
Their bodies merge into it and then various images manifest
in the light. The first image is of Knum, a god with the
head of a ram, who is sitting at a pottering wheel. Instead
of a pot he is forming the body of a woman. It is Aset. From
this single body he creates a double. It is Nebethet. The
next image is a woman entering the private chamber of Asar.
At first it looks like Aset and then it becomes obvious that
it is Nebethet.

                NEBETHET
        (one hand on the
        door, talks to
        herself)
How can I be doing this? It is as
if there is a force pushing me,
compelling me. What is this
powerful desire in my heart?

An ethereal image of Ra appears behind her. He is wispering
in her ear.

                RA
I am the lady of the earth.

                NEBETHET
I am the lady of the earth,
nature is my domain. All that comes into
nature must die some day.

                RA
I am the devotee of Asar. I must
be with Asar now.

                NEBETHET
I am the devotee of Asar. I must
be with Asar now. I am the lady
of the earth, the goddess of worldly
existence and death. I am devoted
to Asar.

Nebethet walks into the room. Asar did not know who it was
and made love with her thinking she was Aset. Asar gives her
a garland in the dark and she leaves the room. In the next
image Aset then sees a great battle between two warriors. One
of them is a young man and the other is Set. Then she sees
the young man injured and lying on the ground. Then she sees
the young man on the throne of Egypt. The next image is the
glory of Egypt in the dynastic period with Akhenaton and

Tutankhamun. Then the Roman soldiers come into view, marching
through the city of Abdu and then Christians carrying crosses
and praising Jesus. Then the Arabs praising Islam through the
streets. The next image is the downfall, all is in ruins, the
Sphinx up to the neck in sand and the next image is modern
Egypt, the city of Cairo with the Arab peoples. The next
image is the resurgence of Egyptian culture in the future. A
woman can be seen seated on the throne of Abdu with clothing
that is a cross between Ancient Egyptian and futuristic
clothing with kente accents. The final image is dissolution
of the earth and the return to the watery state of misty
space which opened the movie. Then, after a few moments of
silence and peace, Aset sees Ra again i his human form.

> ASET
> Oh divine one, it is you who
> control all events and who guide
> the lives of your children, the
> people of the earth and the gods
> and goddesses. Nebethet united
> with Asar for her love but also
> at your insistence. She is the lady
> of mortal existence and it was
> Asar's time to leave this life
> and go to the next. Oh glorious one,
> you are behind all of these
> events on earth and in the heavens. It
> is you who mold all situations so
> that souls may learn and grow
> from their struggles. Oh exalted one,
> allow me to praise you, allow my
> to glorify you and your wisdom.

> RA
> There is yet one last thing for
> you to know, and now you are
> ready.

ON RA'S FACE

Ra closes his eyes and slowly, his face fades -morph- away
and Aset's face appears in its place. She opens her eyes and
says: "I am Ra." Suddenly she emerges from her reverie and
finds herself sitting in the holy of holies in her temple.
Realizing what she has learned from her vision she has a new
resolve.

> ASET
> Everything is connected because
> all comes from one God, one
> source. Sister and I are the self
> same nature, we are one. I must
> help her. The soul of her child
> is like my very own.

She rises herself slowly and bows towards the altar, turns
and walks out of the room slowly.

> FADE OUT:

INT. BIRTHING CHAMBER

Aset walks into the Meskhenet room. Nebethet is lying on a bed. There are several priestesses attending on her. Aset's high priestess walks up to Aset.

                HIGH PRIESTESS
       My lady, the time is now very
       near.

Aset moves towards the bed. With the help of the priestesses she brings Nebethet to a special area of the room. It is a slab with the head and neck of a woman on one end. As soon as Nebethet steps on the slab the head begins to move and speak.

                MESKHENET
        (in an ethereal voice)
       Hmmm...Ahhh...

The priestesses and Aset bow to the head. It is goddess Meskhenet. They praise her and greet her.

                ASET
       Greetings and salutations to the
       goddess of birth and karmic fate.
       We are honored with your
       presence.

                MESKHENET
       Aset, lady of wisdom, this is an
       auspicious day. I know of your
       plight and the sorrow in your
       heart but this hour is for
       rejoicing.

                ASET
       Dear lady, director of souls,
       what
       do you mean?

                MESKHENET
       This very hour will bring the
       birth of a great soul.

                ASET
       Tell me, great lady, you who
       direct the incarnation of souls.
       What is the fate of this soul
       whom you are guiding into this world?

                MESKHENET
       His name will be Anpu. He is
       blessed by Ra with the gift of
       knowing right from wrong. He will

help you in your sacred task to
find Asar.
The time is near, place lady
Nebethet in the right position
and await the precious arrival. This
birth will be easy and painless
since it is Ra's will which is
manifesting.

Aset and the priestesses move Nebethet into position. She
begins to squat down and two servants are holding her arms.
Aset is in front, looking at Nebethet's glowing abdomen.

                    HIGH PRIESTESS
          Look, look...

                    PRIESTESS
          It is so beautiful, the birth of
          a god.

Aset takes the child and brings him to his mothers chest. He
is beautiful as all children are.

                    ASET
          Behold, sister, the fruit of your
          union with Asar is here.

                    NEBETHET
          Sister, you know?

                    ASET
          Yes, I know all, and I
          understand.

The two ladies look at the child with smiles of joy,
forgetting their plight for the moment.

                              FADE OUT:

INT. THRONE ROOM DAY

                    SET
                    (sitting on the
                    throne - rings for
                    servant)
          This is what I have worked for.
          This is my rightful place.

          I should have been the king from
          the start and not that fool
          brother of mine. People do not
          deserve compassion. They are not
          worthy of respect from a god like
          me. I will rule the earth and I
          will show everyone how an iron
          fist can teach people as well as
          kindness. People will obey me or

I will do to them what I did to
Asar.

Enter servant.

> SERVANT
> (bowing)
> Oh gracious lord, what is thy
> bidding?

> SET
> Where are lady Aset and Lady
> Nebethet?

> SERVANT
> I am sorry my lord, we have
> searched the entire palace and
> they cannot be found.

Set becomes angry and lunges towards the servant, hitting
him.

> SET
> You dare to use the word "cannot"
> in my presence? Whatever I decree
> can be done or you will all suffer
> the consequences of disobedience.
> Leave at once and do not return
> until you find them.

> SERVANT
> (holding his injured
> face)
> Yes, yes my lord at once.

> SET
> (to himself)
> You cannot escape me. I will find
> you and you will be my queens.

ON SET'S EYES

                                        FADE OUT:

EXT. TEMPLE OF ASET DAY

Aset and Nebethet look out from a window in the temple and
see now a child of about 8 years of age playing in the
temple courtyard.

> NEBETHET
> Dear sister look at this child of
> ours. Soon he will be fully
> grown.

> ASET

Yes. The mysterious ways of the
spirit are indeed wondrous...
Soon we must leave here. It is not
safe now even here.

                NEBETHET
How soon?

                ASET
We must leave this very night.
Our mother, Nut, will cause a great
darkness to come over the earth.
No one will be able to see. That
is, no one but Anpu. He will lead
us on the path which will take us
to safety.

                NEBETHET
Praises be to the Divine. Our
faith in Ra is never
disappointed.

EXT. TEMPLE OF ASET NIGHT

Aset, Nebethet and the child Anpu, now equivalent to 14 years
of age, leave the temple. There is a procession of temple
servants and priestesses which are following behind them,
escorting them as they move towards the shore of the island
where the temple is located.

                ASET
Priestesses and loyal servants of
my temple. You have risked your
life in helping us this day and
you have achieved Ra's favor.

Your place in the next world is
secure, therefore, fear not for
whatever the future may bring is
god's will for the good of the
earth.

They board a beautiful sailboat. As they raise the sails
they immediately fill with air and the small sloop begins to
move.

                NEBETHET
Oh, beautiful child of mine, tell
us where the path leads to truth
and success. Show us the way to
find the lord of blackness so
that we may bring him back to the land
of light and save the world from
the tyranny of Set.

                ANPU
Dearest mother mine, we must head

north along the path of the Nile
and stop nowhere until we reach
the end of its flow and enter the
great sea. I will point in the
direction to follow so that you
will not meet with any danger or
lose your way on the journey.

Aset takes the tiller and directs the boat.

                ASET
     I will set the course. Now we you
     must rest, sister, for a great
     task is ahead of us.

In the silence of the night, Aset remembered the day that she
and Asar sailed on the Nile and she recalled the image of
Sebek and his promise to help in their time of need. After a
short while, a watery noise was heard. Aset took a spear in
her hands and looked over the side of the barge, where the
noise was coming from. Out of nowhere, a figure emerged from
the murky waters and jumped on board. Aset began to lunge at
the figure but then recognized a familiar shape. It was the
crocodile god Sebek.

                SEBEK
     Dear lady, it is me, your humble
     servant, Sebek. I have come to
     assist you in your quest.

                ASET
              (with a smile)
     Noble sir, I am happy to see you
     on this night of silent
     journeyings. We are on course to
     find Asar and bring him back to
     Egypt. Your help will be greatly
     appreciated.

                SEBEK
     And who is this bright young man?

                ANPU
     I am Anpu, great sir. I am the
     knower of all ways and paths and
     the friend and follower of the
     King of Egypt.

                SEBEK
     Our path is safe and secure with
     the lady of wisdom and the knower
     of the ways. Our journey cannot
     fail.

                              FADE OUT:

INT. THRONE ROOM DAY

Set now proclaims himself as king of Egypt and he summons
the peoples from other lands to his court.

>   SET
>   Listen to me all of you! There is
>   a new king in the land of light.
>   Asar has left for ever and has
>   placed me in charge of the world.
>   Now that I am king there will be
>   some new edicts for you to follow.
>   Anyone who does not follow them
>   will receive the penalty of death!

The gathered crowd is shocked at hearing those words and
everyone looks at each other in disbelief.

>   SET
>   Silence, silence, I am the master
>   here, therefore, you will pay your
>   tributes to me! You will bring
>   your children and women to me and
>   they will be my slaves from now
>   on. You will bring me all of your
>   gold and place it at my feet.
>
>   You will stop all efforts to build
>   schools and cities the way Asar
>   taught you, since you will no
>   longer need them.

Two of the nobles from the crowd shouted out in protest.

>   NOBLE #1
>   What is the meaning of this! This
>   is not the tradition of Asar, the
>   path of Maat. This is injustice,
>   it is against the laws of Maat!

>   NOBLE #2
>   How can there be justice when
>   there is greed in the land? These
>   new rules are the desires of a
>   greedy king!

The crowd began to rise in anger and disbelief. Then Set
stood up and shouted in anger, assuming his wrathful form as
the mythic figure of a man's body with the head of a wild
animal cross between a jackal and an aardvark.

>   SET
>   (yelling)
>   Does anyone dare oppose the king?
>   Who has had the audacity to speak
>   out in this way to the sovereign
>   of the world?

As soon as he finished speaking Set raised his arms up over
his head and the atmosphere in the room clouded over.
Lightning flashed and touched his hands. Then he pointed at
Noble #1 and disintegrated him where he stood. The crowd
stepped back from the place where the horrible murder had
just happened. Then Set continued to speak.

> SET
> (in a soft sarcastic tone)
> Does anyone else have concerns
> that they would like to express?

The crowd fell silent, and the women were weeping and the
children were crying.

> SET
> Silence, silence, lest you feel
> more of my power! Go now and tell
> everyone what you have seen.
>
> Tell everyone what will happen if
> I am opposed. Go now and follow my
> commands or you will meet the same
> fate as this fool who is now gone
> forever!

The crowd streams out of the room. One courtier whispers to
another.

> COURTIER #1
> Why has our lord, the righteous
> Asar, left us in the hands of
> this
> tyrant?

> COURTIER #2
> Also, where are Lady Aset and
> Lady Nebethet and Lord Djehuti in our
> time of need? Is there nobody to
> help us now?

> COURTIER #1
> I fear the worst. I think they
> are either dead or have been enslaved
> by Set.

> COURTIER #2
> Pray we must to the benevolent
> Ra.
> Only he can save us from this
> evil power which has gripped our good
> land.

EXT. SHORES OF SYRIA DAY

The sail boat approaches the shores of Syria. The passengers
disembark an take a look around.

>   SEBEK
>   Queen Aset I will look about the
>   area and make sure that we are
>   safe.

Sebek leaves the area. Aset turns to speak to Anpu, who is
now a young man equivalent to fourteen years of age.

>   ASET
>   Come here young man. You have
>   brought us along way with great
>   skill and efficiency. Tell me,
>   where should we go from hear? How
>   will we find the way to the
>   blessed one, my dear husband?

>   ANPU
>   Dear aunt, do you see the small
>   dwelling in the distance?

>   ASET
>   Yes.

>   ANPU
>   There you will find the
>   maidservants of the queen of this
>   land. They will lead you to the
>   knowledge which you seek.

>   ASET
>   Very well, stay hear with your
>   mother and wait for lord Sebek's
>   return. Then make your camp here
>   and wait for my return.

Aset walks up to the dwelling and before approaching it she
transforms her clothing into that of an ordinary person. She
finds some women there.

>   ASET
>   Greetings to you all, may the
>   blessings from the most high be
>   upon you all.

>   HEADMAIDSERVANT
>   Who are you and whence do you
>   come
>   from?

>   ASET
>   My name is Tesa and I am on a
>   quest to find truth.

The maidservants looked at each other and wondered at the puzzling answer.

                    HEADMAIDSERVANT
          You are not of our land and yet
          there is something familiar about
          you.

The maidservants comes closer to Aset.

                    HEADMAIDSERVANT
          What is the source of the most
          pleasant aroma which emanates
          from your skin?

                    TESA
          I cannot speak of the origin of
          this odor but if you would like
          me to I will impart it to you so
          that you too will be pleasing to all
          whom you meet.

                    HEADMAIDSERVANT
          Yes, please do so with all haste.

Aset begins to braid their hair and prepare special baths
for them. She rubs their bodies with special ointments. Very
soon they are all relaxed and joyous of heart. They are all so
taken with her that they forget the passage of time.

                    TESA
          The pleasant fragrance of the
          body comes from the free and easy
          heart. One who is internally at
          peace radiates a positive
          emanation which can be felt by
          others who are sensitive to it.
          Therefore, always carry joy in
          your heart and you will emanate
          sweetness and goodness to all.

                    MAIDSERVANT
          Great lady, how can we be joyous
          if we do not have that which we
          desire? Even if we get something
          we want, we never know when it may
          be taken away. Life is always
          uncertain.

Aset (Tesa) pauses before answering. She looks out in the
distance, thinking of Asar, and then turns back to answer.

                    TESA
          Joy is not an object of desire,
          but a feeling in the heart. You
          must discover that which is true,

everlasting and pure.

Then you will know what you should
desire. When you find this you
will never lose it and it can
never be taken away from you.
                 MAIDSERVANT
But how do I know what is
everlasting and pure?

         TESA
Look above and see our father, Ra, the sun.
From him we learn great wisdom of life.
He traverses the heavens from time
immemorial, is he not
transcendental and pure? Look at
the earth. The earth has brought
forth life from the beginning of
time is it not transcendental and
pure? All that is fleeting in
this earth cannot bring happiness and
all of the desires that are
unrighteous will some day be
frustrated. Nothing in this
world lasts for ever. Not even the gods
and goddesses can escape this
rule. It is the way of nature.
Therefore, love what is eternal
and true. Then you will never
want for anything and you will always
have bliss.

         MAIDSERVANT
Tell us, wise lady, what should
we desire most in life and how can
we avoid pain and sorrow?

         TESA
Desire for wisdom, peace,
understanding and love. But most
of all, desire after the spirit,
for the spirit is immortal and
eternal and the body is temporary
and fleeting. The soul within you
and in those whom you love is pure
and transcendental. The body is
only a temporary vessel of the
soul. So love all souls and the
one who created them.

Whoever learns this lesson will
never know sorrow and whoever does
not heed this lesson will know
only pain and unhappiness.

The ladies nod in agreement and praise Aset's wisdom.

The Myth of Asar Aset and Heru

> HEADMAIDSERVANT
> Great lady, we must leave now.
> Our mistress, the queen of this land
> awaits our return and we are now
> very late. We will return in a
> while to enjoy your company and
> counsel once more. Until then
> please stay and enjoy this humble
> shelter of ours.

Aset(Tesa) agrees and lays down to rest. She falls asleep.
After some time, suddenly she is awakened by an urgent call.
It is the head maidservant who has returned.

> HEADMAIDSERVANT
> Lady Tesa, lady Tesa please wake
> up. Please wake up.

> TESA
> Yes, you have returned so soon.

> HEADMAIDSERVANT
> Yes. I am here with the queen.
> She wants to meet you herself.

Aset rises slowly and exits the dwelling. Before her stands
a noble lady who is dressed in what is undoubtedly considered
royal dress in this land but what would be considered the
dress of an ordinary person in Egypt.
Her face has kind features and her ethnic appearance is that
of an Egyptian. Aset bows to the lady.

> TESA
> Greetings, noble lady. I am
> honored that you would come here
> to meet me. How may I serve you?

> QUEEN OF SYRIA
> I have heard much about you since
> my maidservants returned to the
> palace.
>
> The intriguing aroma that you
> imparted to them has also
> captivated my attention. You have
> also spoken wise words and they
> cannot speak of anything else but
> you, such a strong impact it is
> that you have had on them.

> TESA
> I have only spoken the truth as I
> learned it my lady. I am on a
> quest of truth.

The queen looks at Aset in the form of Tesa.

> QUEEN OF SYRIA
> I do not know who you are really
> are but your noble bearing and
> wise intellect tell me that you
> are extraordinary and pure of
> heart.

> HEADMAIDSERVANT
> Mistress, I believe that lady
> Tesa would be ideal for the position
> you have been searching to fill.

> QUEEN OF SYRIA
> Humm...perhaps you are right.

The queen stares at Aset for a moment.

> QUEEN OF SYRIA
> Lady Tesa, I have just recently
> given birth to a prince and am in
> need of a nurse to take care of
> him. Could you fulfill this task?

> TESA
> I would be most honored great
> lady. How old is he?

> QUEEN OF SYRIA
> He is sis months old. Come with
> me, we will go to the palace at
> once and you will see him there.

The queen and Aset and the maidservants leave to go to the
palace.

INT. PALACE OF THE QUEEN OF SYRIA MORNING

The ladies arrive at the palace and the queen gives
instructions to the headmaidservant.

> QUEEN OF SYRIA
> Prepare the guest quarters for
> our new arrival. Lady Tesa, please
> follow me to the nursery room
> where we will find my son.

INT. NURSERY ROOM NOON

As soon as the door opens the maidservant walks up to them
with a healthy baby in her arms.

> MAIDSERVANT
> (bowing)
> Greetings, my lady.

> QUEEN OF SYRIA
> Greetings. This is lady Tesa and

she will now take care of the
young prince. Please show her
where all the things she will
need may be found. Lady Tesa, I will
see you later, at the appointed
hour of the evening meal. Now I
must attend to the affairs of
State. So I will see you later
on.

       TESA
Until then, Hetepu, peace be with
you my lady.

The maidservant laid out some linens of the child's bed and
then turns to Aset, who is sitting with the child who is
sleeping in her arms.

       MAIDSERVANT
Lady Tesa, is there anything else
that I can get for you.

       TESA
No, I have everything now. You
have been most kind.

The maidservant exits the room and Aset begins to chant to
the child.

       ASET
Amma su en pa neter...sauuk su
emment en pa neter... au duanu
ma...quedi pa haru...

She paused for a moment. Then she continues singing as she
walks over to the fire, which the maidservant started in a
pit at the center of the room. She then places the child on
the fire. Neither the child nor her hands burn. She leaves
him there suspended within the flame and then she walks away
and continues chanting.

       ASET
Dua Ra, Dua Ra Dua Ra Khepe-ra...
Dua Ra, Dua Ra Dua Ra Khepe-ra...
Dua Ra, Dua Ra Dua Ra Khepe-ra...
Sa anhk mes heh...
Sa anhk mes heh...
Sa anhk mes heh...

       CUT TO:

INT. PALACE OF THE QUEEN OF SYRIA DINING HALL - EVENING

       KING OF SYRIA
Dearest, where is this new maid
that you have spoken to me about.
Your words of praise for her have

made me anxious to meet her. I
also long to see the face of the
prince. Where are they? The hour
of dining has long passed.

>   QUEEN OF SYRIA
>   (with a puzzled look)
> I will go to the nursery myself
> to
> find the cause of her lateness.

INT. NURSERY ROOM

The queen enters the room and is immediately shocked at the
sight. She sees the prince being roasted in the fire and a
strange bird flying close to the ceiling. She screams in
such a horrified manner that the entire palace is alarmed.

>   QUEEN OF SYRIA
> Aaahhhh...Aaahhhh...The prince is
> dying, the prince is dying!

The queen continues to scream uncontrollably and when the
palace staff and the king arrive at the room the prince
suddenly begins to fall towards the burning coals.

The bird immediately swoops down and catches the child in mid
air before it touched the coals and brings him to safety. The
bird begins to transform itself before their eyes into the
form of Aset and she is immediately recognized by the king,
who prostrates himself before her. Aset then walks up to the
frightened mother and delivers the child into her waiting
arms.

>   ASET
> Do not be afraid, your child is
> safe.

>   QUEEN OF SYRIA
>   (sobbing)
> Who are you? What is the strange
> power that you have?

>   KING OF SYRIA
> This is the goddess of wisdom and
> the light of Egypt. She is none
> other than Aset. Adorations to
> you, oh divine lady of truth.

All present bow to Aset.

>   ASET
> Yes, I am Aset.

                    QUEEN OF SYRIA
        But lady, why did you conceal
        your identity?

                    ASET
        I am on a journey, as I told you
        before, and I could not risk
        being discovered. I am searching for my
        husband, who was murdered. I have
        been led here by the tidings of
        fate and I believe I will find
        him in your land.

                    QUEEN OF SYRIA
        What were you doing to our son?

                    ASET
        Your son was not harmed. I was
        purifying his body so as to make
        him immortal.

        Since the ceremony was interrupted
        he will not be immortal but will
        have a long, healthy life. Please
        help me in my quest. I am
        desperate and lost otherwise.

                    KING OF SYRIA
        By all means my lady we shall
        help you on your quest. Every resource
        of my kingdom will be yours to
        find the lord of blackness. But
        how will we know where to look?

A silence comes over them and suddenly the king speaks.

                    KING OF SYRIA
        What is the unique odor I
        perceive?

He walks closer to Aset.

                    KING OF SYRIA
        It is you. The glory of your
        personality and the goodness of
        your soul emanate for all who are

        devoted to wisdom and goodness. I
        noticed the same odor in the
        special pillar that I have
        installed in the palace hall.

                    ASET
        Where is this pillar? Please show
        me without delay.

                         KING OF SYRIA
          Follow me and I will take you
          there.

The king, the queen and Aset go to the place where the
pillar is located. As soon as she looked at it she knew that

Asar

was within it. Only she could see the coffin within and the
body of Asar which was wrapped in bandages as a mummy.

                         ASET
                    (teary eyed)
          It is he, it is he, my dearly
          beloved is found!

                         KING OF SYRIA
          Please tell us my lady, how did
          your husband, the great king of
          Egypt meet such an end as this?

                         ASET
          My lord, greed, deceit and
          avarice are the cause of this injustice.
          Ignorance of the source and
          destiny of the soul is the source
          of all pain and sorrow. Our
          brother, Set, has turned to
          deceit and murder to satisfy his
          desires and this is the result.
          Please allow me to take my
          husband and I shall go in peace.

                         KING OF SYRIA
          Of course my lady I shall have
          the pillar removed at once. But what
          will you do now? Where will you
          go?

                         ASET
          Oh noble sir, I worry not over
          what will come next because I
          feel in my heart that I am being
          guided from above. Even now when the
          struggle of life is most intense,
          I am comforted to know that all
          around me are those striving for
          truth and righteousness.
          Therefore, I am not alone. I am
          hopeful that somehow this will
          all workout for the best.

EXT. PALACE OF THE QUEEN OF SYRIA ENTRANCE-EARLY EVENING

The pillar has been detached from the palace and it is being
carried by Sebek horizontally on his back as Aset bids the
royal family goodbye.

KING OF SYRIA
Are you sure that there is no
other service we can provide?

ASET
No, you have done so much for me
already. You have preserved my
husband and kept him safe. I will
be forever grateful to you and
your family.

Aset turns away and begins to walk towards the place where
the sailboat is located. Sebek follows her.
She arrives at the place where the boat is and finds
Nebethet and Anpu there. They rush to greet her and hug her.

ANPU
Dear aunt, I am so happy
to see you!

NEBETHET
Adorations to Ra, you have
returned to us safely!

NEBETHET
What is this magnificent
object you have found?

ASET
It is the vessel of the soul of
our beloved king, it contains the
body of Asar. Upon reaching these
shores the chest which carried
his body embedded itself in the
ground. Loving him so, his father
Geb grew up a tree which encased
it and the king, liking its
fragrance, cut it and made a
pillar for his palace. Dear Anpu,
you have performed a wonderful
service for our lord. From now on
you will be known as "the opener
of the ways" and all who search
after the truth will revere you
and follow your example for all
time.

They all gather around the pillar with upraised arms and
chant in unison:

"Dua Asar, Dua Asar, Dua Asar, Dua."

ASET
Let us set sail for our homeland.
The darkness will keep our return
secret. Anpu, please assist Sebek
in loading the pillar onto the
boat. Place it securely at the
bow.

ANPU
    Yes, my lady.

They set sail on the Mediterranean sea. The water is calm
and the sky is clear. The star Sirius shines unusually bright
among the vast ocean of stars.
Aset sits quietly next to the pillar with one arm on it as
if hugging it. Lady Nebethet walks up to her.

NEBETHET
    Sister, here is some spelt bread
    and barley wine. You have not
    eaten for some time and you must
    remain strong. Are you alright?
    Do you need anything else?

ASET
    Thank you dear sister, I am
    surely in good hands with you looking
    after me. I will stay here for
    the remainder of the voyage.

NEBETHET
    Anpu has set the course for the
    rest of the journey. We will
    arrive in Egypt just before dawn.
    I will be down below if you need
    me.

Nebethet smiles compassionately at Aset and Aset returns the
smile with one of her own. The two ladies kiss each other
and hug each other. Nebethet stands up silently and goes to the
interior of the barge. After a few moments Aset begins to
cry over the pillar.

ASET
    (sobbing)
    My lord, what will I do without
    you? With all of my wisdom and
    cunning I am still hurt by your
    absence. Even though I know you
    are not destroyed I am still
    mourning your passing.

    Before you go to the final journey
    to the beautiful western horizon,
    the land of Amentat, please come
    to this devotee of yours for one
    last time. Soothe her heart so
    that she may have the strength to
    face the future.

Within a few moments a CRACKING SOUND becomes audible. It is
the pillar. It begins shaking and the sound gets louder.
Aset steps back. Suddenly, it opens up and the chest becomes
exposed and the sound and movement stop. Aset comes closer
to the open pillar and views the contents. The coffin is

glowing with an intense golden color. Aset stretches inside to
open it. Slowly she opens the top of the coffin and reveals the
body of Asar, wrapped in mummy swathings.

                    ASET
          Asar, look at what has become of
          you. The one who brought peace,
          civilization and art to all the
          nations of the earth. He who
          cared for all people as if they were
          his own children, the king of the
          land of light, look at what has
          happened to you. Would you return
          to me beloved? Would you come
          back for one more meeting of love? How
          can you leave before your work is
          done on this earth? I will help
          you to return. Our love will save
          the land and bring peace to the
          world!

Aset closes her eyes and slowly raises her arms. As she
raises them, wings begin to emerge. Then she begins to flap
her wings back and forth and lifts herself up into mid air.
Hovering over the coffin she begins to descend on it. The air
being blown from her wings is full of particles of light
energy which surround the mummy of Asar. Suddenly, the mummy
begins to move and Asar opens his eyes as Aset descends upon
him completely and wraps her arms (wings) around him in an
embrace of love. In the sky above, the three main stars in
Orion's belt become brighter. Then the star Sirius becomes
even brighter. It becomes so bright that it that it floods
the entire scene.

The two of them suddenly appear in the dinghy on the Nile
river, sitting and holding each other as lovers.

EXT. NILE RIVER DAY

                    ASET
          Beloved one, you have returned to
          me!

                    ASAR
          Yes my love. Your devotion has
          brought me back one last time. Do
          not grieve for me dearest, I am
          beyond all pain and sorrow. The
          death of my body was decreed by
          the plan of Ra.
          So there is no reason to harbor
          regret or resentment.

                    ASET
          Oh, dear one of my heart, what
          will happen to our beloved land,
          the Egypt that we knew?

                    ASAR
          Like all things it will be
          transformed by the events of its
          history. But do not worry, our
          sacrifices will not be in vain.
          Sacrifice is indeed the way to
          blessedness. Even the gods and
          goddesses must sacrifice
          themselves so that souls may see
          the righteous path.

                    ASET
          But how will our sacrifice rid
          the earth of the tyranny that has
          befallen it?

                    ASAR
          Our union will bring forth a great
          soul who will challenge the evil
          of Set and free the world again.
          You must remain strong and
          faithful, for the child will need
          you in a most important way. You
          will be his teacher, mentor and
          spiritual counselor in my absence.

          You will teach him the mysteries
          of the world and those of the
          heavens as Djehuti and Ra taught
          us both in days past. In time his
          greatness will be recognized by
          the world and future generations
          shall remember him as the savior
          of humanity.

                    ASET
          Dear lord, your words are indeed
          soothing to the heart. Let us
          savor this time as if it were the
          last moment of creation...

The setting is the same as their last ride on a dinghy in
scene #12 (SAILING ON THE NILE AFTERNOON) But this time it
is Asar who is nestled within Aset's bosom. She is embracing
him with her winged arms.

                                        FADE OUT:

EXT. NILE RIVER DELTA-DAWN

Light from the sun begins to creep up the horizon and the
silhouette of the boat is now barely visible. A soft breeze
is gently pushing it along. Anpu walks forward to the the
place where Aset and the pillar are. He notices that the
chest is open and that the body of Asar is exposed. Aset is
seated in a cross-legged position at the very front of the

bow of the boat, facing out towards the sea. The breeze rushes
through her braided hair and it makes sounds like a wind
chime.

                    ANPU
          Adorations to you my lady, we are
          approaching the shores of
          Ta-meri.
          What is your command?

Aset opens her eyes slowly and turns to him. She is
exhibiting a deep calm in her face, a renewed determination
and inner peace.

                    ASET
          Young man, set a course for the
          papyrus swamps. We will remain
          there amongst the tall reeds
          until the appointed time comes.

Anpu turns and goes to the stern in order to set the right
course. Nebethet arises from down below and looks for her
sister. Seeing her she goes to her. She pauses a moment to
look at Asar and then sits beside Aset.

                    NEBETHET
          Good morning sister.

                    ASET
          Dearest Nebti, I will need your
          assistance on this day.

                    NEBETHET
          What is it sister? Are you ill?

                    ASET
          No. I am supremely filled with
          hope and...

                    NEBETHET
          And what?

                    ASET
          I am with child.

                    NEBETHET
          Praises be to Ra. How is this
          possible?

                    ASET
          The wisdom I learned from Ra
          allowed me to bring back the life
          of the body of Asar. His soul
          came to visit me one last time during
          the night.

                    NEBETHET
          Wonders are many in this universe
          but your powers never cease to
          amaze me.

                    ANPU
          There it is, the land of light!

The boat approaches the shores of Egypt. They find a spot to
disembark and then begin to walk inland.

                    NEBETHET
          We must find a suitable place to
          make our camp. Anpu go before us
          and find the best place. Sebek
          bring the body of our divine
          king.

Anpu transforms himself into a jackal and runs off into the
rushes. Sebek turns into a crocodile and carries the mummy
of Asar on his back.

                    NEBETHET
          Come sister, I will help you.

The two ladies walk together for a time. Then, after some
time they hear a noise and take cover.

                    ANPU
          My ladies, where are you? It is
          me, Anpu.

                    NEBETHET
          We are here.

                    ANPU
          I have found a suitable place for
          our camp. It is secluded and far
          away from all paths and it is not
          far away.

                    ASET
          Let us make haste, the appointed
          time is drawing near.

EXT. CAMP IN THE PAPYRUS SWAMPS -AFTERNOON

They move on and reach the place chosen by Anpu. Anpu and
Sebek make the camp while Nebethet makes Aset as comfortable
as possible. After a short while, the two ladies begin to
hear a rustling sound.

                    ASET
          Sister, what is that noise?

                    NEBETHET
          I am not sure. It seems to be
          coming from there.

Pointing towards some reeds. Nebethet begins to walk towards
that place but is suddenly surprised when she finds that a
cobra has come out into view. She steps back.

                    NEBETHET
          Sister, it is a cobra.

                    COBRA
          Ssssssssssss....sssssssssss......

Before they could have any further reaction the cobra began
to enlarge itself to the size of a human being.

Then it transformed itself into a beautiful, voluptuous
woman. She begins to speak in a low, sexy but elegant voice.
Her movements are serpentine as she walks towards them.

                    UADJIT
          Greeettiings, I am Uadjit.

                    ASET
          Greetings Uadjit. I am so very
          pleased to see you.

                    UADJIT
               (prostrating at their
               feet)
          Adorations to you my lady. I am
          the one who is blessed with the
          vision of you and your sister.

                    NEBETHET
          Uadjit, how did you find us?

                    UADJIT
          I was drawn here by a special
          feeling that my mistress was near.
          I know of your plight and I am
          here to help you. I will construct
          a special arrangement of foliage
          and reeds which will afford the
          greatest comfort and safety to
          Lady Aset.

                    NEBETHET
          Very well. Rest here now sister.
          I will return soon with water.

After a short while Nebethet returns with some water and sits
down next to Aset. Uadjit, after completing her task, also
sits down.

NEBETHET

Aset, the time for the birth
is nearing. This place will be safe
for a while but where will we go
after this?

UADJIT

My ladies, if you desire, you may
go to my temple in the serpent
city. You will be safe there for
as long as you need. The
priestesses are devotees of mine
and of yours as well. They will be
honored to take care of you all
and see to your needs.

ASET

You are most gracious and kind,
dear Uadjit. We will certainly
accept your offer.

UADJIT
            (bowing her head
My lady, it is my pleasure to
serve you, especially in your time
of greatest need. I will stay here
and help you and Nebethet through
the delivery. Now, great lady, you
must get some rest, for the time
is nearly upon us.

Aset laid herself down on the bedding as Nebethet and Uadjit
stayed at her side and rubbed her feet (reflexology) and
massaged her legs to comfort her and prepare her for
childbearing. Then, after a short while, they all hear a
familiar sound. It is the sound of a chorus chanting Amun...
Amun... Amun... Amun...She looks everywhere but initially
sees nothing. Then a golden light appears before her and two
male figures come into focus. They are the Gods Amun and
Djehuti. Upon recognizing them Aset prostrates herself. Sebek
and Anpu rush over and also pay homage to the vision that
they see.

DJEHUTI
            (to Aset)
No, no my child, there is no need
for that at a time like this.
Remain comfortable in your place.
We have come to assist in the
nativity, to bless you and the
newly incarnating soul.

AMUN

Dua Aset, Dua Aset... Greetings
and salutations to the first lady
of wisdom.

                    ASET
Lord Amun, I am blessed by your
presence.

                    AMUN
No my child, I am blessed to be
here at this moment in time to see
you give birth to the light of the
world. The duty of all gods an
goddesses is to show the way to
blessedness and not to
unrighteousness.

In this task you are a model for
all. You are adored in the heavens
and on earth as well.

Amun raises his hand and the sky opens up with a vision of
dozens of gods and goddesses with upraised arms in adoration
of Aset. In response, Aset raises her hands up to them.

                    ASET
Tell me lord Amun, you who bring
the hidden essence of the spirit,
what is the nature of this child
who comes to me with such regard?

                    AMUN
The child who will be born to you
will be known as the light. His
name will be Heru. He will bring
back to life the soul of your
beloved Asar and challenge the
evil which has taken over this
world.

                    DJEHUTI
This child will be raised as a
philosopher and as a warrior by
you in accordance with the way
that I have taught you in days
past. You must teach him and
protect him until the time when
he will challenge the evildoers of
the world.

                    AMUN
Now my dear child, it is time for
the birth.

They see a bright light emanating from the abdomen of Aset.
The birth has begun. Amun points his Uas scepter and touches
Aset's head with it. A shower of light-energy bathes her
body. Djehuti raises his arm. In his hand he holds an ankh
amulet and he touches Aset's mouth with it. A light energy
stream is transferred from the instrument to Aset's body.
Nebethet moves closer to Aset. She then reaches down and

95

picks up the newborn child and holds him up for everyone to
see. The stars in the heavens sparkle, especially Sirius.
Wind blows through the trees and a deep chorus brings forth
a chant in unison: Dua Heru Ra Ta ... Dua Heru Ra Ta...Dua
Heru Ra Ta...Dua Heru Ra Ta...!(Adorations to Heru, the light
of the earth...) Lady Nebethet looks at the child's eyes. She
looks into his right eye and sees the sun. Then she looks
into his left eye and sees the moon.

                    NEBETHET
                 (with amazement)
        Oh!

Nebethet now carefully hands the baby over to his mothers
waiting arms.

                    ASET
                (smiling, with tears
                 in her eyes, whispers)
            Dua Heru Sa Aset...
            Dua Heru Sa Asar...
            Dua Heru Raah Taah

MOVE IN AND FOCUS ON MOTHER NURSING THE CHILD

                                        FADE OUT:

INT. THRONE ROOM DAY

Set is sitting at the throne, talking with one of his
servants.

                    SET
            I am bored with the palace. What
            am I to do with all of these
            insignificant people around me!
            Is there no excitement left for me?

                    SERVANT
            Master, shall I bring your harem
            or the Nubian dancing girls to
            entertain you?

                    SET
            No. I am bored with them as well.

                    SERVANT
            Perhaps a hunting trip will
            entertain you master. I am told by
            the papyrus makers in the north
            lands that a giant boar has been
            seen in the area. Surely he will
            be a challenge for you and will
            bring you many hours of
            entertainment pleasure.

             SET

You have spoken well. Prepare my
hunting equipment. I will leave
at once!

EXT. CITY LIMITS NORTH-DAY

Set stands at the north end of the city with two servants.

             SET

Let us move on now. I am anxious
to find the famous giant boar
which is roaming freely in the
papyrus swamps. I will end his
freedom and make of him my
evening dinner.

The three men begin to walk up the path. Set moves ahead of
the two men.

             SET

Hurry you two, I do not want to
lose the light left for the day.

             SERVANT #1

How disgusting, eating the meat
of hogs.

             SERVANT #2

Yes, I agree. Set is the only one
of our people who eats swine.

             SERVANT #1
             (chukling)
Perhaps that is why he has such a
bad disposition.

The two servants smile at each other, covering their faces so
as not to be seen and then scurry to catch up with Set, who
is now at some distance ahead of them. Set wipes some sweat
from his brow and looks up at the sun.

             CUT TO:

EXT. NILE RIVER DELTA (PAPYRUS SWAMPS)-DAY

Anpu is looking up at the sun and then turns to Aset, who is
holding the child Heru by the hand. He is a beautiful baby
boy with copper brown skin and healthy, proportionate body
features. He is standing on his own now and equivalent to the
age of one year. Djehuti and Amun have left. Sebek is
constructing a shrine around the pillar, which contains the
coffin and body of Asar. The pillar is upright. It has four
tears above the section which contains the body.

             ASET

Anpu, search the area for some
firewood please.

> ANPU
> Yes my lady, at once.

Anpu leaves the area and Nebethet approaches Aset with some
bed clothes for her and the child.

> NEBETHET
> Uadjit has just left. She will
> prepare the temple for our
> arrival.

> ASET
> It is good to know that in our
> time of need there are so many
> who are willing to help.

> NEBETHET
> Aset, did you ever think that our
> lives would change so much? Just
> a short time ago you and I and
> Asar were in the throne room,
> watching the people from all over
> the earth visit us just to pay
> homage to you and Asar.

> ASET
> Yes I know precisely what you
> mean. Life has so many strange
> twists and turns. Sometimes it is
> difficult to know the path and at
> any moment we may be taken away to
> the next life.

> NEBETHET
> Like Asar.

> ASET
> Yes.

> NEBETHET
> How is it that you are so strong?
> How is it that you seem to know
> the best path and never deviate
> from it?

> ASET
> (with a chuckle)
> No, no sister I am not perfect!
> Sometimes I too feel lost.

> NEBETHET
> Then how do you manage to wade
> through the waters of worldly
> troubles? What secret do you have

which allows you to move forward
even when all seems lost?

          ASET
There is a secret of sorts which
I hold onto at all times.

          NEBETHET
Tell me sister, so that I too may
live under this protection as
well.

          ASET
Dear Nebti, it is a secret only
because people do not think
deeply about life. I am known as the
goddess of wisdom. Do you know
why?

          NEBETHET
No sister, please tell me.

          ASET
It is because long ago I was a
mortal woman. I was ignorant of
the name of Ra and his glory and
I set out to learn all that I
could learn about the world. It
was an exiting time. I learned the
secrets of nature, the ways of the
human body and how to heal it, the
revolutions of the stars, the
special words of power to control
nature and much, much more. Still
I could never satiate the desire
in my heart to know the cause for
my existence and the reason for
pain and suffering.

          NEBETHET
What did you do then sister?

          ASET
Then I reflected within myself.
What is it that I truly seek
after? If I want knowledge I could
continue living like this forever
and what will I gain thus?

Is there nothing more substantial,
more abiding to be sought in life?

          NEBETHET
What happened then sister?

          ASET

Then, as you know, one day, I saw
Ra traversing the heavens as he
usually does in his barque of
millions of years and I decided
to ask him this important question.

           NEBETHET
I recall the vision that lord
Djehuti allowed me to see but I
do not remember Ra answering these
questions. What did he say?

           ASET
Ra said nothing because the
answers to these questions cannot
be given through speech. So he
showed his true nature to me and
this experience transformed the
way I look at everything. Now
everything I think or do is with
this new feeling. Now I have peace
and inner harmony in my heart for
all eternity.

           NEBETHET
Sister, show me how to attain
this most exalted wisdom. Show me the
way which leads to blessedness
and peace.

           ASET
I will surely show you the way
dear sister mine, at the
appointed time of your enlightenment.

Nebethet looked at her sister with a puzzled expression. The
two ladies become silent as Aset brings Heru to her breast
and begins chanting to him. An echo of the chant fills the
area with a wonderful feeling that brings a smile to them all.

EXT. NILE RIVER DELTA (PAPYRUS SWAMPS)-AFTERNOON

Set is hot on the trail of the wild boar.

           SET
Aahh... now I have you. You will
not escape me now. I, Set, the
king of this land, will take you
as my prey and display you in my
throne room.

Set spots the boar and begins to aim his bow and arrow
towards it. The boar suddenly turns in his direction and
sees him. The boar dashes away in the opposite direction. Since
he has lost the shot, Set begins a hot pursuit of the
frightened animal.

EXT. NILE RIVER DELTA (PAPYRUS SWAMPS)ASET'S CAMP-
AFTERNOON

The atmosphere is calm. Everyone is resting from the days
events. Suddenly, Anpu lifts his head in attention. Aset,
Nebethet and Sebek notice his agitation.

                         SEBEK
               What is the matter?

                         ANPU
               I do not know. I believe I hear
               something coming towards our
               direction.

                         NEBETHET
               What is it?

                         ANPU
               I think it is a wild boar.

                         NEBETHET
               What did you say?

Before he could respond a great rustling could be heard in
the bushes nearby. Suddenly, a largely overfed member of the
swine family charged through their camp as if pursued by
death itself. Anpu, Nebethet, Sebek and Aset were motionless
as the boar passed by. It was so fast that it was gone as
fast as it appeared.

                         SEBEK
                    (laughing)
               Well that was something.

Anpu once again went into attention.

                         ANPU
               Wait.

                         SEBEK
               What is it, another boar?

                         ANPU
               No, this creature is larger.
               Everyone, take cov...

Before he could finish the statement an imposing figure ran
into the encampment. It was Set. The surprise of the moment
caused them all to be still for a few moments which seemed
like hours. Then Set dropped his bow and arrow when he
realized what he was seeing. Then he spoke. His words were
like fire and his anger was beyond his control.

                         SET

                    (pointing to the
                    pillar
What is this? What is this? I
destroyed that one and sent him to
the bottom of the Nile. So this is
where you treacherous ladies have
been hiding from me. Now I will
end your lives once and for all
for defying me.

Sebek and Anpu place themselves in between Set and the two
ladies.

                    SEBEK
Set, turn away from the ways of
evil and egoism, they will lead
to your ruin in the end!

                    SET
Do not lecture me you slimy
reptile. Crawl away while you
still can before I decide to
destroy you as well.

                    ANPU
                    (turning to the
                    ladies)
You must leave now with the child
and take him to safety.

                    NEBETHET
                    (distraught
No my son, I cannot leave you in
this danger!

                    ANPU
You must do as I say. You must
save Heru at all costs. The
future of the world depends on it. Go
now while you still can. We will stop
Set for as long as we can.

                    SET
                    (shouting)
Do not speak to me with your
useless philosophy of right and
wrong Sebek. Right is when I get
what I want! Think before you
speak, young one. Are you ready to
leave this world? Stand aside and
live or meet your doom at my hands.

                    SEBEK
What kind of king is this that
speaks threats and boasts? Who is

this unrighteous man with no
concern for anyone but himself?

As the three combatants have the exchange of words, Aset,
Nebethet and the child slip away into the tall brush. Set
begins to transform himself into his wrathful aspect. Sebek
transforms his head into that of a crocodile and Anpu
transforms his head into that of a jackal. Sets hands become
metal claws with sharp points.
Into Anpu's right hand a sword appears. Into Sebek's right
hand a spear appears. Set moves forward to deliver the first
blow. Sebek blocks him and then Anpu attacks Set. The
contests goes on for some time while the combatants exchange
blows. They had no effect on Set and he became angrier.

> SET
> I have been playing with you just
> as a child plays with toys. Now
> you will see the real power which
> I possess.

Set steps back from them, closes his eyes and a small tornado
appears around his body. Anpu and Sebek look at each other in
awe of the sight. Suddenly, Set opens his eyes and directs
the force of the whirlwind towards the two combatants. Anpu
and Sebek are lifted off their feet and they land some
distance away, unconscious from the powerful blow.

Set now moves towards the pillar. He punches it and it cracks
into pieces, leaving the coffin completely exposed.

> SET
> Now I shall finish what I
> started.
> Aset should never have defied me
> by finding you and bringing your
> body back here. I am the rightful
> ruler of this land and I will
> remain so forever!

Set lifts the chest and flings it into the air. Then he
produced a ball of fire in his right hand and directs it
towards the coffin which explodes into fourteen pieces that
spread all over the world.

ON SET'S FACE

> SET
> So you have a son do you? If I am
> to remain as king he too will
> have to experience the same fate as
> his father.

Set rushes over to the place where he last saw the ladies
and the child and finds that they are gone. Then he begins to
shout after them.

                         SET
          Do not think that you can escape
          from me. I am the master of this
          earth and I will find you
          wherever you may hide.

Set begins to let out a terrible roar which is chilling to
the weak of heart. It can be heard for miles away.

                                        CUT TO:

Aset and Nebethet stop and turn around as they hear the
disquieting bluster of Set.

                         ASET
          Come sister, we must move on
          without rest. Our safety depends
          on it.

They turn around and continue moving on. Suddenly, they hear
rustling in the bushes behind them.

                         ASET
          Sister, I fear that Set is coming
          closer. Do as I tell you without
          question or delay. Take the child
          and move on while I venture off
          and attract the attention of Set.
          This will give you the time to
          escape his evil designs.

Nebethet takes the child. They give each other one last look.
Aset kisses Heru and sends them on. Aset then makes noise as
she runs in a different direction, trying to attract the
attention of Set. She is successful but at the price of her
own capture. Set suddenly pounces from out of nowhere and she
stops so as not to run into him. She cuts through the brush
to no avail. He pounced in the middle of her path again.

                         SET
                    (smugly)
          It is no use, you cannot escape
          me. Where is your sister and the
          child?

Aset remains motionless but her eyes are on fire with anger.
Set walks up to her.

                    SET
Why do you oppose me? You know I
am the stronger one. I am the
smarter one. It was I who
cleverly tricked Asar into getting into
that golden coffin and he never
suspected a thing!

                    ASET
He did not suspect you because he
had faith that you would change
your ways, that you would honestly
seek his friendship. But even I do
not know what is in your heart any
more. What happened to you? Long
ago you were the protector of the
weak and the teacher of sacred
martial arts, the benefactor of
all and the servant of Ra. Why
have you fallen into disgrace?

                    SET
I will tell you my dear. I grew
tired of serving others and I
decided that I am the one who
should be served.

                    ASET
Service is a noble calling. I am
the servant of my lord and of all
who seek wisdom.

                    SET
What lord? That mummy? He is no
more. You will never find him now.
Therefore, surrender to me and
serve me from this day forth and
I will spare your life. Tell me
where your son is so that I may
find him and train him to serve me.

On hearing this Aset looks down so as to hide her sorrow.

                    ASET
                 (looking up in
                  defiance)
I will never surrender to you. I
will never serve evil and greed.
I am the servant of honor, truth
and justice and nothing else. I
will never tell you where he is.
Some day he will become a warrior
of Maat and he will make you
answer for all the evil things you
have done.

                    SET

The Myth of Asar Aset and Heru

                    Do not speak to me of your weak
                    philosophy. You and your son will
                    die like Asar. You are my slave
                    as of this moment!

Suddenly, rope bindings appear on Aset's wrists. They are
tethered to a rope which Set is holding. He yanks on it to
pull her forward.

                         SET
                    You will be my prisoner until you
                    change your mind.

Set pulls her away, into the brush.

                                        FADE OUT:

EXT. CITY OF THE COBRA GODDESS-DAY

Nebethet gets away safely and arrives in the city of the
cobra goddess, Uadjit. There she finds shelter in the temple
of Uadjit and takes care of Heru, who is now a child of 3
years of age.

She knocks at the doors of the temple and is greeted by the
High Priestess there, who prostrates herself at Nebethet's
feet as soon as she realizes who it is she is addressing.

                    HIGH PRIESTESS
                    Greetings dear lady, Adorations to
                    you. It is my good fortune to see
                    you! We were alerted as to your
                    impending arrival by our mistress,
                    Lady Uadjit.

                    NEBETHET
                    May the light of Ra fall upon you
                    all your days and may you enjoy
                    life, health and strength always.

                    HIGH PRIESTESS
                    Thank you for your blessing my
                    lady. Come in and rest. You seem
                    to have been on a long, arduous
                    journey.

                    NEBETHET
                    Yes that is true.

                    HIGH PRIESTESS
                    I will take you to the room where
                    you can rest with the child.

The priestess leads Nebethet to a large room. Several
priestesses walk in carrying water, fruits and linen.

                    NEBETHET

It is essential that you keep my
presence here a secret. I was
being pursued by an evil of
unspeakable power and Lady Aset...
I do not know what has happened to
her.

                    HIGH PRIESTESS
I understand my lady. A messenger
came yesterday from Abdu and told
of the horrors which the people
there are suffering at the hands
of Set. People everywhere are
afraid since he may come to any
city and do the same.

                    NEBETHET
We must guard this child with our
lives. He is the only chance for
the salvation of the world.

                    HIGH PRIESTESS
             (turning to Heru with
              a smile and tickling
              his cheek)
Who is this precious young one of
Blueish-black complexion?

                    NEBETHET
He is the son of Aset, the lady
of wisdom, and Asar, the lord of the
perfect black.

The two ladies turn to look at the child, who is now
exploring the room.

                    HIGH PRIESTESS
Fear not my lady. The power of
this temple is great in repelling
the evil and unrighteous. You
will be safe here for as long as you
may need to stay.

INT. CITY OF ABDU PALACE -DAY

Meanwhile, Aset has been made a prisoner in her own palace.
Set has had her confined to her quarters with a guard posted
outside. Aset walks across the room in silence, looks out a
window, which now has bars on it, and views the sun. Then she
closes her eyes and begins to pray.

                    ASET
Oh, benevolent Ra, who watcheth
over thy Creation, assist me in
this time of need. Locked away am
I in this prison of my own design.

108

Is there a way to become free of
this burden? May the rays of thy
light illuminate my heart so that
I may see the path before me.

A few moments of silence pass and suddenly, a light begins
to shine in the center of the room. A mist emanates from it and
it takes human form. It is Lord Djehuti.

> DJEHUTI
> Greetings be to the foremost
> devotee of truth and wisdom.

> ASET
> (smiling)
> Uncle, how good it is to see you!

Aset prostrates herself before him. He embraces her and
raises her.

> DJEHUTI
> (sarcastically)
> How is it that the symbol of
> wisdom is imprisoned as a common
> criminal. The times are indeed
> reversed and the laws of Maat are
> ignored as a passing breeze.

> ASET
> Lord Djehuti, my son is...

> DJEHUTI
> Safely out of danger for now
> but...

> ASET
> (with concern)
> But what great sir?

> DJEHUTI
> The child needs his mother if he
> will successfully meet the
> challenges that is before him.

Aset turns away from him.

> ASET
> How will I be able to reach him
> now that I am in this condition?

> DJEHUTI
> What is your problem?

> ASET
> Please do not taunt me uncle, I
> am prisoner here, with guards to
> prevent my escape.

The Myth of Asar Aset and Heru

                    DJEHUTI
          The queen of this land, the lady
          of wisdom, should not be hampered
          in any way. Set is away from the
          palace and the guards are in a
          deep sleep which has overcome
          them. You must leave now and seek
          out your son. To protect you I
          have summoned seven scorpions.
          They will accompany you and guard
          you on your path.

          Hide yourself well and your son
          will grow strong in body and
          wisdom. He will need these
          qualities and more for the
          challenge which lies ahead.

                    ASET
          Thank you uncle, but how will I
          know where to find my son?

                    DJEHUTI
          You will find him safe at the
          place where the coils of my staff
          meet together.

which
Djehuti shows Aset his caduceus staff. It has two serpents

intertwine in an upwardly spiraling manner and their heads
meet at the top. Bowing, Aset utters a final benediction.

                    ASET
          The temple of Uadjit. Thank you
          uncle. Hetepu, Peace be with you!

Djehuti returns the bow and Aset leaves the room. Aset moves
stealthily along the hallways and corridors of the palace
and finds everyone asleep. When she exists the palace
entranceway she begins to run. When she reaches the city limits
seven large golden colored scorpions suddenly appear just as

lord
Djehuti promised.

                    ASET
          Come along, followers of the lady
          of wisdom, for there is a long
          journey ahead.

INT. TEMPLE OF UADJIT - DAY

The High priestess walks into the room where Nebethet is
resting.

                    HIGH PRIESTESS
          My lady, my lady please wake up.

Please wake up.

                    NEBETHET
               (groggy)
          What is the cause of your
          agitation?

                    HIGH PRIESTESS
          The child, the child.

                    NEBETHET
          What is wrong, where is he?

                    HIGH PRIESTESS
          He is in the palace garden. He is
          amongst the temple mascots, the
          serpents, of the goddess!

The two ladies rush to the garden. Nebethet finds Heru, now
equivalent to the age of a child of 6 year of age, playing
innocently with dozens of asps, cobras, and an assortment of
other snakes.

                    NEBETHET
          Heru, Heru come to me and leave
          the garden at once!

                    HERU
          But auntie, I am having fun with
          my friends.

                    NEBETHET
          Please Heru come at once!

                    HERU
               (reluctantly)
          Very well.

Nebethet takes his hand and looks over his body to make sure
there are no marks and finds that he is alright.

                    HERU
          Why are you looking at me that
          way auntie?

                    NEBETHET
          I was worried for you my son. I
          though that the serpents might
          hurt you.

                    HERU
          They are my friends. They told me
          about the goddess of the temple.

                    HIGH PRIESTESS
          Adorations to Ra!

Nebethet looks at the priestess with a puzzling look.

> HIGH PRIESTESS
> This is indeed an auspicious day.

> NEBETHET
> What do you mean?

> HIGH PRIESTESS
> The last time such an event like
> this occurred was when the young
> prince Asar, no older than master
> Heru, visited this temple with his
> mother, the goddess Nut, a long
> time ago. In the same manner he
> too consorted with the serpents
> and was thereby blessed with the
> secret wisdom of the Life Force.
> This is surely a sign that Heru
> has a special destiny to fulfil
> and it is a good omen indicating
> success.

Nebethet turns to Heru with a reassured and compassionate
smile.

> NEBETHET
> Come inside now young man. We
> will prepare a special bath for you
> now and then we will go to the temple
> to pray for the safety of your
> mother, Lord Sebek and your
> cousin Anpu.

Nebethet takes Heru by the hand and they enter the temple.

INT. CITY OF ABDU PALACE -DAY

Set returns to the palace and sees the guards outside
asleep.
He pushes one of them and they fall over. He walks inside
and finds that all his guards and servants have been overcome
and that Aset has escaped.

> SET
> (exceedingly angry)
> What is the meaning of this? The
> best guards in the land, overcome
> by a mere woman. How can you be
> fit to guard the palace if you
> cannot even remain awake? I should
> send you to die in the desert
> lands this very moment as a
> rewards for your failure.

They begin to wake up and find Set extremely angry.

                         SET
          You are all incompetent and lazy.
          You have failed me for the last
          time.

Set produces a ball of fire and raises his arm in
preparation to strike them down. A servant comes rushing into
the

hall.

                         SERVANT
          Master, master have mercy please.

                         SET
          Mercy? You do not deserve to live
          any longer! Give me one reason
          why I should spare you.

                         SERVANT
               (shaking with fear)
          I have come to know just
          recently,
          that Lady Aset was seen as she
          made her escape.

                         SET
          Where is she now?

                         SERVANT
          She was seen leaving the city by
          the west and then heading to the
          north.

Set withdrew the fireball and thought aloud.

                         SET
          Hmm...she must be attempting to
          find her son and lady Nebethet. I
          will send a special demon against
          them. He will not fail to rid them
          from this world.

Set stretches out his arms in front of himself with palms
facing upwards. Suddenly, a large red scorpion appears,
suspended above his palms.

                         SET
          By my power I command thee to go
          north and follow the trail of
          Aset.

          Search out the son of Asar and
          Aset and inject him with your
          venom and end all life in his body!

Set places the scorpion on the ground and it immediately
exists the room. The servants are in awe of Sets awesome

power and they step back to make a path for the scorpion.

EXT. CITY OF THE COBRA GODDESS-AFTERNOON

Aset finally reaches the city by late afternoon. Seeing the temple she heads for it immediately. Upon reaching it she knocks on the doors.

> PRIESTESS
> Who desires to enter the dwelling
> place of the cobra?

> ASET
> It is I, the lady of wisdom and
> the mistress of the black land.
> Please open at once, for my
> journey has been long.

Immediately, the doors of the temple open wide and upon seeing Aset the high priestess prostrates herself before her.

> PRIESTESS
> Please forgive me, mistress of
> Creation. I was not sure of who it
> might be and in order to protect
> our esteemed guests I was afraid
> of opening our doors without being
> sure of who it was seeking
> entrance.

> ASET
> Fear not, loyal servant of
> Uadjit.
> Your actions have been pure and
> in accordance with Maat. The goddess
> has noticed your actions and it
> pleased. Tell me, is there a
> certain young boy here?

> PRIESTESS
> (with a smile)
> Yes my lady, young master Heru,
> the playful one, is here.

> ASET
> (humorously)
> Well, he has acquired a new title
> I see?

> PRIESTESS
> (smiling)
> Yes mistress, in his short stay
> with us he has become the very

essence of cheeriness and good
nature. Everyone here is taken
with him. So powerful is his
charm.

            ASET
Please take me to him at once.

            PRIESTESS
Yes my lady, follow me.

Aset follows the priestess. They walk through the main
courtyard and into the Hypostyle hall. There they find a
side room. Heru is inside with several priestesses. Some are
playing with him and laughing while others are attending on
him with food, clothing and so on. On noticing her, Heru
immediately runs up to her and wraps himself around her legs
in an ecstasy of joy. He is now equivalent to 10 years of
age.

            ASET
Adorations to Ra! Feel the grip
of this child! You have become
strong in my absence!

            HERU
        (looking up at her)
Mother dearest, I have been
waiting for you so long. Why did
you delay?

            ASET
        (squatting to his
         level and hugging
         him)
I was detained for a while but
now I am free and will never leave
your side. Come tell me all about
your stay here. I want to know of
all of your adventures.

As they walk out of the room, Heru begins to talk.

            HERU
Mother, I have discovered that
all animals are my friends. The
pylons of the temple were created ten
thousand years ago, the
priestesses pray to the goddess
every hour and...

            ASET
Slowly, slowly my son. There is
so much to tell and so much to hear!

INT. BED CHAMBER -NIGHT

                    ASET
          Come, dearest child of mine. It
          is time to sleep.

                    HERU
          Mother, why do we sleep?

                    ASET
          We all must sleep because
          sleeping allow us to have peace in our
          heart.

                    HERU
          What is peace?

                    ASET
          Peace is the feeling of freedom.
          There is no confusion, no
          fighting, only joy in the heart.

                    HERU
          What is joy?

                    ASET
          Shall I tell you all of the
          secrets of life on this very
          evening? It is not enough time.
          Sleep now and tomorrow your
          instruction will commence.

Aset tucks Heru in his bed and begins to sing to him.

                    ASET
          Amma su en pa neter...sauuk su
          emment en pa neter... au duanu
          ma...quedi pa haru...
          Dua Ra, Dua Ra Dua Ra Khepe-ra...
          Dua Ra, Dua Ra Dua Ra Khepe-ra...
          Dua Ra, Dua Ra Dua Ra Khepe-ra...
          Sa anhk mes heh...
          Sa anhk mes heh...
          Sa anhk mes heh...
          Dua Heru Maa kheru...
          Dua Heru Maa kheru...
          Dua Heru Maa kheru...

Heru falls asleep and Aset's voice gradually becomes softer
and lower. When she finishes the chant she lays her head down
beside Heru and closes her eyes.

                                        FADE OUT:

EXT. CITY OF THE COBRA GODDESS-DAY

                    ASET
          Today, dear son of mine, we will
          go into the city. There you will

see the great shrine to Asar which
has been constructed by the people.

Nebethet and the high priestess wave to them as they leave
the temple. As they walk through the streets of the city.
Heru was taken with all that he saw, the buildings, the
people. Then he saw some other children playing and left his
mother's side to join them. Some men and women noticed her
and recognized her and the goddess Aset. They ran up to her
and sought her blessings. Aset touched them on their head and
blessed them and then noticed something strange as she looked
in the direction where Heru was. Suddenly, the children that
he was playing with began to run away in fear. She knew that
something was wrong.

                    ASET
               (moving
                 towards him)
          Heru, Heru, come here my son!

Then her greatest fears came to pass. Heru fell to the
ground. Aset reached him and picked him up.
Nearby she saw a large scorpion walking away and with a
fiery look she burnt it to ashes.

                    ASET
               (distressed)
          Heru, Heru speak to me.

It was of no avail, Heru's was foaming at the mouth due to
the poison of the scorpion. She rushed back to the temple.

INT. TEMPLE OF UADJIT, BED CHAMBER - DAY

                    NEBETHET
          Sister, what has happened to
          Heru!

                    ASET
               (sobbing, lamenting)
          Heru is bitten, the heir of
          heaven, the son of Asar-Un-nefer is
          bitten, the child of the gods, he
          who was wholly uncorrupted, is
          bitten! He for whose wants I
          provided, he who was to avenge his
          father, is bitten! He for who I
          cared and suffered is now
          dead! -sobbing- I am Aset, who
          conceived a child by her husband,
          and became heavy with Heru, the
          divine one. I gave birth to Heru,
          the son of Asar, in a nest of
          papyrus plants. I rejoiced
          exceedingly over this, because I
          saw in him one who would make
          answer for the injustice done to

his father. What will happen now?
What will be the fate of our land?
My beloved one is dead. I have
lost my love a second time. Is
there no end to the cruelty of
this world?

                NEBETHET
Sister, can you utter words of
power to eradicate the poison
from the body of Heru?

                ASET
            (sobbing)
The words of power which I
possess, are not strong enough to
overcome this poison. Such is the
nature of its power that it could
only have come from Set.

Nebethet began to cry as well. Aset remained at Heru's side.
Nebethet left the room, so painful was the scene there. It
so happened that the goddess Selket had come to visit the
temple. She was greeted by the high priestess and found
everyone in mourning.

EXT. TEMPLE OF UADJIT - ENTRANCE - DAY

                HIGH PRIESTESS
            (with a heavy heart)
Greetings my lady. We are honored
to see you.

                SELKET
Tell me, my child, what is the
matter? What is the cause for
this gloom which has befallen the
temple of the great serpent?

                HIGH PRIESTESS
            (sobbing)
Unspeakable it is, unspeakable!

Selket notices the severity of the situation and consoles the
priestess. Nebethet entered the courtyard where they were and
recognized the exalted newcomer.

                NEBETHET
            (in mourning)
Dear cousin of mine, I am pleased
to see you.

                SELKET
Tell me, great lady of the earth,
what sorrow has overtaken this
temple? What manner of evil has

pushed away the joy of life in
everyone here?

          NEBETHET
The light has left us, stricken
down by an evil curse.

          SELKET
What do you mean cousin?

          NEBETHET
Heru, the son of Aset has been
poisoned and he is now dead and
gone!

The two ladies fell silent. Then Selket turned to lady
Nebethet with hope.

          SELKET
Where is the child and his
mother?
Take me to them at once! There is
a chance that all is not yet lost
but we must hurry for time is
fleeting.

Nebethet leads Selket to the place where the dead body of
Heru is lying in state. There they find Aset at his side
sobbing.

          ASET
Lo, I was a mother to the child,
and now I sit here, powerless. Is
there any greater pain than the
loss of one's own being? How can
the light of the world be taken by
a mere scorpion? The fate of
suffering is my lot to bear. When
and where will it end?

          SELKET
What is this you say, the sting
of a scorpion has caused this
sorrow?

Aset turns and notices Selket. A ray of hope has comes over
her as she stands up and walks over to Selket.

          ASET
Dear cousin, the mistress of
scorpions. Surely you know some
special words to eradicate the
poison and bring my dear one back
to this world.

Selket walks over to the bed and examines the body.

                    SELKET
Dearest one of my heart, there is
nothing that I can do. The poison
has taken its toll and the child
is lifeless.

                    ASET
          (looking up)
How is this possible, lord
Djehuti, you had promised that a
strong and healthy child would he
be. Was there some fault in your
words or in their reading?

                    SELKET
Lord Djehuti, said this prophecy?

                    ASET
In deed he did.

                    SELKET
Then dear cousin the solution to
this curse is clear.

                    ASET
What do you mean?

                    SELKET
You are the mistress of healing
and only you can save your son
now.

                    ASET
But I have already tried and my
incantations have no effect.

                    SELKET
There is no incantation you can
utter which will bring the young
one back to life.

                    ASET
Then what must I do?

                    SELKET
You cannot heal the child alone
but you have the power call upon
the one who can help you.

                    ASET
Who must I call?

                    SELKET
The barque of Ra traverses the
heavens daily.

> Detached and aloof it is from the
> affairs of the earth, is Ra, even
> though he sustains life on earth
> through his very radiance of Life
> Force energy. There is only one
> soul on this earth who can attract
> the attention of the most high and
> divine one; the one who has
> discovered his essence.

Aset stood frozen for a moment and remembered the vision of
her communion with Ra. Then she knew what had to be done.

FOCUS ON MOUTH OF ASET

She began to utter Ra's name in such a way that the entire
room began to vibrate. The SOUND of her voice became louder
and louder.

                    ASET
          RRRRAAAAAAHHHH........

ON ASET FROM ABOVE

As Aset uttered the name she looked up. The sound of her
voice carried up to the heavens and the royal vessel, the
barque of Ra, which was moving along placidly, began to rock
and then it came to a standstill. With this halting of the
barque, so too the entire creation came to a standstill. the
people in the cities, the animals, the breeze, the Nile
waters all stopped dead in their tracks. Ra was sitting on
his throne and Djehuti was standing in front of him facing
forward. On the bow of the ship was a female figure with a
feather on her head which was held in place by a headband.
She was sitting on the bow of the ship facing forwards. Her
name was Maat. Noticing the turbulence, Maat turned to Djehuti.
                    MAAT
          Lord Djehuti, there is a
          disturbance in the heavens and on
          earth, such as has never been
          seen since the time of Creation. Time
          and space have come to a
          standstill, the waters of the
          Nile move no more. The wind blows no
          more and we cannot move forward.

                    RA
          What is the nature of this
          disturbance?

                    DJEHUTI
          It can only be the sound of thy
          name, majestic one.

Ra stands up and waves his hand in front of himself. An
image suddenly appears of the sorrowful scene of the deathbed
of Heru.

RA

Behold, See what calamity has
befallen the lady of wisdom and
the young child of light! The air
has left his nostrils. There is
no life in him.

MAAT

It is the wickedness of Set which
is responsible for this
inauspicious event. Pride, egoism
and greed have taken over the
earth and now its grip has taken
the life away from the young son
of Asar. It is not right for the
good to be destroyed by the evil.
It is against all righteousness
that love and compassion should be
rewarded with pain, sorrow and
death.

RA

I will make restitution of this
life and with it the struggle for
the good will continue. For this
is the way of nature which I have
set forth wisely from the
beginning of time.

DJEHUTI

What is thy bidding my master?

RA

Be on thy way with all haste. Take
with thee the special words of
power which restore life, health
and strength. Go to the young one
who has been stung with the bitter
venom of avarice and sooth the
pain of the mother who bore him
with love and peace.

With this charge Djehuti bowed and disappeared into thin air
as Maat and Ra looked on.

MAAT

Adorations to you father. You are
the greatest champion of truth
and righteousness.

RA

Be thou prepared daughter of mine.
Your assistance will also be
required in due time. You will
teach the young one the value of
virtue and the means to the

practice of righteousness which
will lead him to success.

                    MAAT
          When you command, I will be
          ready.

                                        CUT TO:

INT. BED CHAMBER -NIGHT

Aset and Nebethet were alone in the bed chamber next to the
dead body of Heru. Suddenly, a light appears in the center of
the room. Aset notices the light as it takes form as Djehuti.

                    DJEHUTI
          Greeting dear one. I have come to
          assist you in your time of need.

            ASET   NEBETHET
         (hopeful   (sobbing with hope
     Adorations to Ra,   Salvation has come! Praise
     Adorations to the merciful   be to the lord of the
     inhabitant of the barque   Divine Barque!
     of millions of years.

                    DJEHUTI
          Dearest Aset no harm can possibly
          touch Heru, for I am under the
          protection of the boat of Ra, and
          so are you and this child of
          great destiny.

But his words failed to comfort Aset, and though she
acknowledged the greatness of his words, she complained to
him impatiently.

            ASET   NEBETHET
     With all haste please save   Help him oh great and wise
     the child of light. Save   one. Bring him back to our
     him from the evil fate of   loving arms without delay.
     death and destruction.

Djehuti begins to move towards the bed.

                    DJEHUTI
          Fear not lady Aset. Fear not lady
          Nebethet. For I carry with me the
          great words of power of Ra which
          have the strength to heal the
          child for his mother.

                    ASET
                 (sobbing)
          Oh great one of ancient days,
          what use are the incantations or even
          the great command of Maa-kheru if

the child remains there, lying in
the arms of death. An evil most
vile is this attack, which has
led to his misery and death!

With a compassionate smile, Djehuti looked at the two forlorn
mothers, who had suffered so much. Then he turned and walked
over to the bed. With upraised arms he began to speak.

      DJEHUTI
Wake up Heru, your protection is
established for all eternity. Make
happy the heart of thy mother.
Verily that which is in the mouth
of Ra shall circulate through the
body of the child, and the tongue
of the Great God shall repulse all
opposition to life. For the sake
of this child the boat of Ra
stands still in the same place
where it was yesterday.

Djehuti now holds his hands facing upwards and he is looking
up.

      DJEHUTI
Move on boat of forever. Do not
stand still any longer. Come
forth and transmit your life force to
this child.

The boat of Ra begins to move and a ray of light shines forth
out of the boat and down into the body of Heru. His entire
body is illuminated with golden light.

      DJEHUTI
Heru is counted up for life, and
he is declared for the life of his
father. I have given gladness unto
those who are in the Boat, and you
divine mariners of the boat, make
it to journey on.

The oarsmen of the boat of Ra begin to move again and the
boat travels forward.

      DJEHUTI
Heru liveth for his mother Aset,
and he who was in the pillar will
live likewise. As for the poison,
the strength thereof has been
made
powerless.

Heru begins to move.

      NEBETHET

Look, the child lives. The child
lives!

DJEHUTI
Never fear dearest one. Those who
live with faith and virtue will be
rewarded with miracles. I stand
before you now as Ra's minister
and I decree the following things.
I will take charge of the case of
Heru in the Judgment Hall of Anu
wherein Asar had been judged in
times past. Just as I was his
advocate in days past, so too will
I be the same for Heru. I will
make reply to anyone who would
make any accusations against Heru.
Furthermore, I will give Heru
power to repulse any attacks which
might be made upon him by beings
in the heights above, or fiends in
the depth below. Anyone who
opposes Heru in his bid to regain
the throne of Egypt will have to
face not only him but myself and
the exalted one, Ra himself.

ASET
My heart has been redeemed today
lord Djehuti. Your words have
been followed by deeds of truth and
strength. I am indebted to you as
the savior of my son. Adorations
to you!

DJEHUTI
Dearest one, do not overlook thine
own deeds of valor and
righteousness. It was the words of
power of his mother which have
lifted up his face and they shall
enable him to journey wheresoever
he pleaseth and to put fear into
the powers above. I myself hasten
to obey them. It was you who was
able to stop the grand boat of
millions of years by the power of
your purity. It is that same power
which can caused the dead to be
raised... Therefore, I salute you
and pay homage to you, who are the
example for all in this world to
follow. Because of your exemplary
life and your courage, yours will
be the eventual victory.

With this said, Djehuti vanished and reappeared in the boat.

Maat and Djehuti lift up their arms in adoration to Aset,
who is now holding the child, Heru in her arms. The boat moved
on and faded into the horizon and night fell over the world.

                                                FADE OUT:

INT. TEMPLE OF UADJIT -REFLECTION CHAMBER - DAY

It is morning and Aset and Heru are walking into the special
room where the goddesses study and reflect on the teachings
related to the gods and goddesses. It is filled with candles
and it is dimly lit. Heru is now sixteen years of age.

                    HERU
          Mother dear, what is this place?

                    ASET
          It is called the chamber of
          reflection. The initiates of the
          goddess come here to study her
          teachings and to become wise.

                    HERU
          Tel me mother, what is wisdom?

                    ASET
          Wisdom is understanding the
          secrets of life and then being
          able to live wisely.

                    HERU
          Tell me mother, am I wise?

                    ASET
               (smiling)
          You most certainly will be, dear
          one.

                    HERU
          How does a person become wise,
          mother?

                    ASET
          Wisdom comes from asking
          questions and then reflecting on them so
          that you might understand the
          true meaning of the answer.

HERU

Please mother, help me to become
wise, like you and Lord Djehuti.

ASET

Then you must ask the questions
that lead to the unveiling of the
mysteries of life. So ask your
first question an receive your
first lesson.

HERU

Mother dear, how did the world
begin?

ASET

Long ago the universe was like an
ocean. There was no sun, no world,
no time and no Egypt. Everything
was formless and nameless. All of
this was god's body in his name,
Nu.

Then one day, Nu thought within
his heart, "let me bring form to
this ocean of formless matter." So
then he became the disk of the sun
in his name as Ra, the sun that
sails across the heavens. In his
boat is lord Djehuti, he is Ra's
pilot and the guide of men's
minds. In the front of the boat
sits Maat. She establishes order
and truth in all creation as the
barque moves on. So all Creation
is alive and all creatures are to
be guided by Maat and Djehuti who
represent right action and right
thinking.

HERU

Mother, by what power does Ra
cause plants to grow and the sun
to shine and the body to have
energy?

ASET

The force you speak of is the
fiery eye of Ra. The sun is that
power and it gives life and
warmth to all things.

HERU

What is the name of this force?

ASET

Its name is Sekhem and it is

controlled by goddess Hetheru, the
eye of Ra. So you see my son, Ra
created Maat, Hetheru and Djehuti.
They are the forces that hold this
Creation together and which give
it life. Ra transformed the
primeval ocean, his very own body,
into the universe that we see.

       HERU
What happens if the barque stops
its sailing?

       ASET
Then my son, the universe comes to
an end and all ceases to be with
form.

Order will fall into disorder. The
universe will once more go back to
the primordial state. The end of
Creation will that be.

       HERU
Mother dear, where do human
beings come from?

       ASET
A profound question you have
asked, my son. Proof it is of your
advanced intellect. Ra created all
living creatures including men and
women. In reality all life is
spirit appearing as matter. So Ra
took a spark of his light and gave
it form as the bodies of man and
woman. He took another spark of
his own soul and placed it in the
bodies and so the bodies came to
life through his own breath.

       HERU
But why are some bodies male and
other female?

       ASET
Dear one, you must understand
that sex is a thing of bodies and not
of souls. The soul chooses a body
according to its needs and
desires.

       HERU
And mother why did Ra create
souls and bodies for them to live in.

                ASET
So that they might learn about
the glory of love and discover the
one who created them through the
struggle and sacrifice of human life.

Heru pauses his questioning, closes his eyes and reflects.

                HERU
Mother dearest, why is there evil
in the world and what is the
purpose of suffering?

                ASET
My son, long ago, Ra himself ruled
the earth. It was a time of peace
and joy and harmony and light. For
thousands of years his glory was
revered. He was loved by all the
souls he had given life to. A long
time passed and men and women
became bloated with pride and ego.
They said "Who is this Ra anyway,
we don't need him." People forgot
about him and they forgot that all
people, all over the universe,
were created by the same spirit
and are all brothers and sisters.
So they began to fight one
another. Hatred, anger, greed and
violence were thus born. Therefore
understand my son, evil is the
conceit, selfishness and vanity in
the heart. That is the cause of
evil and pain and sufferings.

                HERU
Tell me mother, how can a person
find peace and harmony and stay
away from egotism?

                ASET
To find peace and harmony and to
stay away from evil there is but
one way my son. It is the path of
virtue, the path of Maat.

                HERU
Please mother, tell me more about
Maat.

Aset was holding heru's hand and suddenly she let go of it
and placed both her arms outstretched at her sides and
closed her eyes. Then a transformation began to take place. She
was turning into goddess Maat. Wings sprouted from her arms and
her head ornament transformed into a feather.

                MAAT
        (in an ethereal voice)
My son, this is my form as the
goddess of truth, order and
righteousness. I sit at the bow of
the barque of Ra and I bring order
to the universe as the barque
traverses the sea of creation. If
a man or woman places me in the
forefront of their life they will
discover truth and harmony in
their life.

                HERU
How can a man or woman place you
in the their life?

                MAAT
I have created guidelines for
righteous living, forty-two in
number are they. Anyone who lives
by these will surely discover
peace and harmony in the world. In
due time this land will adopt
these rules and by their power
this culture will last ten times
one thousand years and more.
Powerful are these precepts. Take
this scroll with the complete
list. Study them and live by them
and you will surely succeed in all
your endeavors. If you fail to
uphold these injunctions your
affairs will surely fail. For
doing good, selflessness, sharing,
and contentment are in harmony
with the universe. Those who are
greedy, egoistic and cruel will,
by my power, surely end in ruin,
since this universe is governed by
the law of cause and effect.
Goodness is repaid with goodness
and evil is punished with
frustration. Listen to my teaching
and follow it in your life. For no
success is possible for one who
does not have self-control.

                HERU
        (bowing his head)
Adorations to you, great lady of
truth and cosmic order.

                MAAT
May you discover peace and
harmony my son.

Maat fell silent and began to transform once more into Aset.

> HERU
> Mother mine, tell me who am I and
> where is my father?

Aset remained silent and Heru thought that something was
wrong because he did not receive a reply.

> HERU
> Mother, please answer me. I must
> know where I come from and the
> fate of my father and the cause
> of his absence.

Once again, silence. After a while a light began to appear in
the room. A male figure came into form as an ethereal spirit.
He is dressed with regal vestments over the mummy wrappings
which are on his body. It was Asar. Aset opened her eyes and
turned to him. He was surrounded by a white aura and his head
appeared half human.

> ASET
> Husband, dearest one, you have
> returned to us.

> ASAR
> Yes my beloved, and I will always
> be with you.

> HERU
> Father, is that you?

> ASAR
> I am Asar, the lord of the
> perfect black.

Heru rushes over to Asar and prostrates himself at Asar's
feet. Asar raises his arms in adoration.

> ASAR
> How fortunate am I to have a
> strong righteous son such as this
> one.

Heru looks up and tries to touch Asar. His hand passes
through Asar's body.

Heru steps back an notices that Asar's head is now
transforming into a that of a hawk.

> HERU
> Father, I cannot touch you.

> ASAR
> No my son, nor can you touch a

dream, and yet it is there in
your mind.

                    HERU
What is this new forms that I
see?

                    ASAR
What you see is my form as Lord Sokar,
the king of the Astral world.
This is my new dwelling place.

                    HERU
Father mine, what is the cause of
your absence from us? What is the
nature of this body of light that
you possess?

Asar looks at Aset and then turns back to Heru.

                    ASAR
Before you were born I was the
king of this great land, but
greed and avarice betrayed me and
killed my physical body.

                    HERU
How was it possible for this to
happen to a righteous soul such
as you?

                    ASAR
As your dear mother explained, in
the time when Ra ruled the earth,
people became arrogant and cruel.
They strayed from the path of
Maat. What your mother did not say
is the rest of the story. Listen
carefully and learn from what
follows.

Ra in his wisdom, sent me, thy
mother, lady Nebethet, and my
brother Set to the world, so that
we might teach everyone how to
live in harmony and peace, to
practice religion, and
civilization and to work for the
good of all. For a long time we
succeeded and the world was at
peace and people learned to love
again. But Set was greedy, he
wanted more than to serve humanity.

Pause

                    ASAR
          Desire swelled in the mind of Set.
          His only ambition was to get what
          he desired. Everything he
          sacrificed, the good works of his
          past, the love for the world and
          for his family and the wisdom of
          Ra as well. For you see, when
          there is anger and hatred and
          desire in the heart, there can be
          no wisdom or understanding or
          peace. Then it is possible for
          such a person to commit sins and
          crimes of unspeakable nature.

Asar paused once more and looked at Aset. Then he turned
back to Heru.

                    ASAR
          What I must tell you now you must
          know for certain. Set in his anger
          and greed killed my body and stole
          the throne of Egypt.

ON HERU'S FACE IN DISBELIEF

                    ASAR
          Yes my son this is true.
          Intoxicated with merriment, song
          and love from all the people of
          the world, I did not realize the
          plot against me until it was to
          late.

          Therefore, vigilant you must be
          and on guard at all times, even
          when you are filled with the joys
          of love and peace, because the
          evil of the ego is stealthy and
          treacherous. Before you become
          aware of its designs it can cut
          you down.

                    HERU
               (heart swelling with
                anger)
          Tell me father what must I do?
          How can I avenge this injustice?

                    ASAR
          You must find peace and harmony
          within and forget all ideas of
          revenge.

Heru looked at him with a puzzled stare.

                    HERU

But father, surely I should cut
punish Set and do to him what he
did to you!

    ASAR
Have you not learned the lesson of
Maat? Never forget, it is said
from ancient times that "Those who
live today will die tomorrow,
those who die tomorrow will be
born again; Those who live by Maat
will not die." My body was killed
but I am not dead. We are not
bodies, but eternal souls.
Therefore, do not become ensnared
in the passion of vengeance and
hatred over me. Hatred brings more
hatred and hatred leads to
violence, not justice. A true
follower of Maat does not act out
of anger but only out of truth.
First you must discover true inner
peace.

    HERU
But father, how will peace help
me to struggle against evil?

    ASAR
The evil in the world can only
exist when there is weakness in
righteous people. So the
righteous must become strong in order to
overcome evil. Since evil cannot
overcome evil, they do this by
discovering the power of Maat
instead.

    HERU
Father, how can I discover the
power of Maat?

    ASAR
First you must understand the
philosophy of life well, that all
Creation is the spirit of Ra. The
spirit of Ra is in you, me, your
mother, as well as in Set.

    HERU
In Set? If this is so, how can he
be cruel and selfish?

    ASAR
He has forgotten these things and
his mind is clouded with the fire
of desire. When your heart is

clear you will know that we are
all one, Then you will never harm
others, lest you hurt your own
heart as well. When you live by
this teaching you will discover
inner peace and harmony. When
there is peace and harmony in the
heart, you will also know the
power of Maat. You must always
stand for truth, even in the face
of criticism evil and violence.
Then you will be ready to confront
Set, who is a mighty warrior.

    ASET
Heed the warning of your father,
my son. If you act like Set you
will become like him and you too
will become a force of evil and
hatred.

In the future it will be said:
"MAAT is great and its
effectiveness lasting; it has not
been disturbed since the time of
Asar. There is punishment for
those who pass over it's laws, but
this is unfamiliar to the covetous
one....When the end is nigh, Maat
lasts." Therefore, trust in Maat,
do Maat and speak Maat always and
your frame will last until the end
of time.

    ASAR
Indeed your mother has spoken
well. Always remember that those
who revere Maat are long lived;
they who are covetous have no
tomb. There is no peace for the
desire-filled heart. One day you
will challenge Set, but you will
do so as a warrior of virtue and
not for personal gain. For there
is glory is fighting for truth
because truth leads to
enlightenment and immortality.
Egoism leads to desire and desires
for the pleasures of the world can
never satisfy the heart. Thus, a
human being who is in the grip of
desire and who is devoid of
righteousness, the ethical basis
of life, will never find true
peace and joy in life. Therefore,
do not stray from the path of

Maat, my son.

A silence fell over the room and then Asar spoke one more
time.

          ASAR
Now we must leave you in silence
to contemplate these great
teachings. Tomorrow you will leave
this temple and you will go to
land of our ancestors, the land of
Ethiopia. There you will be
trained in the art of life and war.

          HERU
Who will train me father?

          ASAR
That you will discover when you
reach your destination.

          HERU
How will I know the place to find
my teacher of the art life and
war?

Asar points to the doors of the room as they open. In comes
Anpu.

          ANPU
I will show you the way my
cousin!

          ASET
Anpu, you are alive! Adorations
be to Ra. I am so joyous to see you.

          ANPU
Yes my lady. After your escape,
Set stunned me and Sebek and when
we woke up Set had left in pursuit
of you. I am so glad that you
escaped and I see that the young
child has safely grown to be a
young man.

          HERU
What has happened? Someone please
tell me.

          ASAR
There will be enough time for talk
on your journey. Now we must leave
you to meditate in silence upon
your lessons of the day. I will
see you again in a short while.

Until then my son heed the words
of your mother and the counsel of
your cousin. I will watch over you
as the sun, during the day, and as
the moon during the night and I
will be also in your heart.

> HERU
> Yes father, by your command.
> Hetepu

Asar disappears into thin air and Aset and Anpu leave the
room quietly. Heru sits in front of the altar and closes his
eyes.

> FADE OUT:

INT. TEMPLE OF UADJIT -REFLECTION CHAMBER - DAY

It is midday and the reflection chamber doors open. Anpu,
Aset and Nebethet await Heru. Heru is now a young man-24
years old- of imposing bearing and strong stature.

> ASET
> Praise be to Khepra. The boy of
> yesterday is no more. A man now
> stands in his place.

Heru prostrates himself at his mothers feet and she blesses
him.

> ASET
> May all your endeavors be guided
> by Maat. May you endure in the
> hearts and minds of all people
> around the world as your father is
> revered and loved. May you
> discover the joy of inner peace.

> NEBETHET
> May your journey be safe. Hetepu.

> ANPU
> Come cousin, we must leave at
> once
> for the journey ahead is long.

EXT. LYBIAN DESERT - DAY

Heru and Anpu are traveling in the desert, southward from
the
lands of lower Egypt to Ethiopia.

> HERU
> Tell me cousin, why do we travel
> through desert lands instead of
> along the Nile?

138

ANPU

It is essential that our journey
remain secret. No one must know
that you are alive, lest the news
may reach the ears of Set.

HERU

You are wise cousin, but tell me,
how do you know your way through
this vast wilderness of sand?
There are no land marks or signs
to determine the way.

ANPU

Ahhh... but you are mistaken.

HERU

Please explain, what signs have I
missed?

ANPU

Do you not see the sun in the
sky, he traverses from east to west
and never changes his course from the
beginning of the day to its
conclusion. In this manner we can
know the hour of the day as well
as north and south. At night do
you not see the stars which are
the ornaments in the body of our
grandmother, Nut?

HERU

Yes.

ANPU

The position of the stars also
let us know the direction we are
following and the hour of the
night.

HERU

You are clever, cousin. With you
as my guide I am secure in
reaching my destination.

In the late afternoon the two come upon an oasis in the
middle of the desert.

ANPU

Behold Heru, an oasis is before
us.
Let us make camp there for
tonight and renew our strength and
provisions. Then we will continue

the journey tomorrow.

They build a fire and sit facing it with eyes closed. The sitting posture is cross-legged with arms on their thighs.

                    HERU
          Anpu, I have learned so many
          things in such a short time. I am
          amazed at the immensity of this
          universe and the glory of Ra as
          well as the glory of my mother
          and father.

                    ANPU
          Indeed, I too am awed and blessed
          to have seen the things that I
          have.

                    HERU
          Sometimes, my mind becomes
          clouded. I do not know which way
          to proceed or how to think about
          things. How can I become a
          follower of Maat if I am not sure
          at all times?

                    ANPU
          It is difficult to know what to do
          in life sometimes. This is why a
          person needs to be guided by the
          teachings of Maat when they are in
          doubt. In time you will learn the
          art of thinking as you practice
          the teachings you have learned.
          Your mind will become calm and
          clear when you practice
          meditation. Meditation sharpens
          the mind and brings clarity as
          well.

They lay down to sleep. Heru looks up at the sky and sees a shooting star amongst the thousands of stars that are visible.

                              FADE OUT:

EXT. OASIS IN DESERT - DAY

                    ANPU
          Heru, Heru, wake up. we must
          leave now.

                    HERU
          When will we arrive at our

destination cousin?

          ANPU
This very day.

They pack their supplies and begin to walk across the desert
once more. They see many desert creatures and even walk
through a brief sandstorm on the way. Then they climb a sand
hill and when they reach the top they view a scene of their
destination.

          ANPU
     Look Heru, our destination is
     near.

          HERU
     It is a vast, beautiful country.
     How much longer will we travel
     before reaching there?

          ANPU
Two more hours.

                                        CUT TO:

EXT. TEMPLE OF BES-LATE AFTERNOON

In front of the main entrance to the temple there are two
great statues of a short man with a large round face with a
beard. His head is leonine in appearance with a protruding
tongue. His ears are large. He is chubby and robust and his
legs are bowed. In one hand he has a sword and in the other
he holds a jug of wine. The travelers reach the apparently
deserted temple and stand outside admiring it. Suddenly, a
figure steps out from behind them. It is a dwarf. He comes in
between them, pushes them aside and continued walking without
a word. Heru and Anpu look at each other and then Heru speaks
to the dwarf.

          HERU
     You sir, how is it that nobody
     has taught you manners?

The dwarf turns around and responds.

          DWARF
     Ha ha ha... teach me will you?

          HERU
Yes I should.

          DWARF
     You cannot teach me anything, you
     are a mere child. Go back to your
     mother and let her teach you. I
     have no time for children. I am

busy.

Heru became annoyed with the short man's insolence and ill manner.

>   HERU
> I will teach you respect sir.

>   ANPU
> Heru, let it go. This man did not
> mean any disrespect.

>   DWARF
> Is the child afraid of a dwarf?
> Ha ha ha. Let it go Heru, let it go
> Heru. Ha ha ha! Go home young
> one, this temple is no place for
> children.

Heru moved towards the dwarf, trying to grab him.

>   DWARF
> Think you can catch me? Ha ha
> ha... think again.

The dwarf drops a bag he was carrying. He is so agile that Heru cannot catch him. Then Heru gets an idea.

>   HERU
> Let us go cousin, I am tired of
> this game. This dwarf is under
> the protection of some special magic
> and he will not fight fairly.

The two turn to walk away. Then the dwarf picks up his belongings and suddenly Heru lunges from fifty feet away in an attempt to grab him from behind as Anpu watches the scene in amusement. But the dwarf is aware of his plan and disappears in thin air at the very last moment. Heru falls flat on his face. The dwarf appears behind Heru and starts to laugh a great belly laugh. Then Anpu also begins to laugh.

>   HERU
> Cousin why are you laughing at
> me?
> I would have expected that from
> this disrespectful dwarf but not
> from you. Oh, my leg is bruised.

>   ANPU
> Please forgive my laughter cousin.
> I am amused by your feeble attempt
> to catch the very one whom we have
> come to see!

The Myth of Asar Aset and Heru

> HERU
> This man is to be my teacher?

> ANPU
> Yes, he is indeed!

The Dwarf walks up to Heru and gives him a hand.

> DWARF
> (smiling)
> Rise up, young one, you have just
> received your first lesson in
> life, Ha ha...

> HERU
> (sarcastically,
> holding his leg)
> I would like someone to explain
> this lesson to me since I am the
> only one who does not know what
> it is but who felt the pain of it
> just the same.

The dwarf suddenly begins to undergo a transformation. He
takes on the appearance of the statues in front of the
temple.

> DWARF
> My name is Bess. I am the god of
> mirth, passion, and war. You have
> just learned that there is no
> profit in fighting over petty
> arguments. What should the
> disrespect of the small minded
> lead you to anger and waste of
> energy? No my son, reserve your
> strength for what is really worth
> fighting for.

> HERU
> Tell me sir, what is worth
> fighting for?

> BESS
> That, my young disciple, is what
> you have come to learn.

> ANPU
> I must leave now cousin, my task
> is finished. I will see you again
> in the fullness of time.

> HERU
> Farewell, cousin, I am forever
> indebted to you.

Heru and Bess walk inside the temple.

INT. TEMPLE OF BES-LATE-EVENING

                    BESS
          Come my son, I will show you to a
          place where you can rest. You
          must get plenty of rest for tomorrow
          will be a big day for you.

                    HERU
          Please tell me, great sir, how
          did you come to be known as the god
          of mirth and war?

                    BESS
          Long ago, in the time when Ra
          ruled the earth, there was no war
          and no struggle. Everyone lived in
          harmony and peace. Even when I was
          in Ra's court, and I was his
          friend and counselor, my wit
          became famous because I could
          always bring a smile to his face;
          That is, until the evil of men
          started and Ra left the earth.

                    HERU
          Then what happened? Please
          continue on.

                    BESS
          Then men and women became ego
          driven and petty-minded. The
          desires of their hearts became
          more important than truth so
          people began to fight one another.
          So I taught fighting to those who
          wanted to fight and life to those
          who want to live.

                    HERU
          Please tell me, teacher, what is
          living and what is its art?

                    BESS
          Living is feeling and doing and
          loving. Living is also suffering
          and sacrifice and dying. Most
          people live but they live like a
          plant or an animal. This is not
          real living. If you learn how to
          see the goal of life then life has
          meaning and joy and not strife.

                    HERU
          Oh exalted one, how can I deal
          with the pain of life?

                    BESS
          Humor is the key to surviving the
          pain of life, my son. In
          everything there is a humorous
          point of view. If you learn how
          to see this you will never be
          depressed, sorrowful or blue.

                    HERU
          Great one, my father has sent me
          to learn also the art of fighting
          from you. What is the use of
          fighting when living is more
          important and true?

                    BESS
          My son, this point is important to
          understand. Even the righteous
          must sometimes uphold the laws and
          make a stand. For if they do not
          show the way to the young, society
          will never learn the path to
          become one.

          Now that we live in an age where
          Ra no longer rules the earth,
          every human being must discover
          his or her own worth. This means
          that people have choices in their
          life, to pursue what is good for
          all or to live in argument,
          conflict and strife. This is why
          for one such as you who will be a
          leader of society, it is important
          to learn the path of philosophy,
          art and history.

Heru paused his questioning for a moment to reflect on what
he had heard.

                    BESS
          Now in silence you must reflect
          on these teachings. Allow them to
          enter deep into your heart and
          let them transform your feelings.
          Tomorrow we will begin your
          instruction on the art of war. So
          sleep well and prepare to learn
          more about who you are.

Heru raised his arms to Lord Bess.

                    HERU
          Adorations to you great sir. Your
          teachings in rime are resounding

in my ears. I will never forget
them for as long as I live.

                    BESS
               (smiling)
          Hetep! Peace be with you!

EXT. TEMPLE OF BES - DAY

Bess and Heru stand in the temple courtyard. Both have
swords as weapons in their hands.

                    BESS
          Your next lesson will be in the
          art of fighting. Never take your
          eyes off the one you are
          contending with.

Heru looked down to adjust his belt. Bess swatted him on his
back side with his sword. Heru yells in pain.

                    HERU
          Hey, I was not ready for that
          attack!

                    BESS
          Ha ha! Learn now you must, not to
          trust your opponent. Otherwise you
          will be caught by surprise and
          finally end up repentant. Always
          vigilant and watchful you must be.
          For the lazy and weak, evil do
          they never see. Be now on guard
          and block my blows. Then you will
          not regret and feel the pain that
          those who get injured do know!

They practiced for hours, trading attacks and practicing
strategy. Finally, at dusk they rest and sit by a fire to
eat.

                    HERU
          Tell me teacher, what is the
          value of laughter? You are so jolly and
          cheerful, even in the midst of
          this world of mixed pain and
          pleasure.

                    BESS
          Ahhhh.... A very good question
          you have asked, my son. The value of
          laughter is best told in song.

Bess begins to sing and dance his teaching. He skips and hops
around the fire. Then to his own surprise Heru begins to
laugh.

                    BESS
          La, la, la, lahh...I am I am the
          warrior of love. The temple is my
          home and the roof the sky above.

Bess trips and falls.

                    BESS
          If I should fall and bring smiles
          to your face. Your heart will be
          happy and cheerful with faith.

Bess climbs a tree and points to a fruit and opens it
exposing the seeds.

                    BESS
          No matter how gloomy the world
          may appear, I look at the wonders of
          life, they are all here. From a
          tiny seed a mighty tree comes out
          of the ground. And then as if by
          magic a fruit falls down.

Bess fell out of the tree and the fruit falls on his head.
Heru is very amused and continues laughing.

                    BESS
          Never forget that life is
          fleeting. So don't waste your
          time with negative feelings.

Bess was about to step on a scarab as he was dancing. He
picks it up and puts it in a tree.

                    BESS
          Discover the joys of life all
          around you. Respect for all
          creatures, big or small, is what
          you should always do. When you
          live in accordance with this
          teaching you will discover, that
          all Creation is god's way of
          spreading joy all over. Those who
          are always serious and somber,
          will never understand the peace of
          laughter.

Bess returns to Heru's side with a smile. Heru is smiling
and clapping.

                    HERU
          Great one, you have released in
          me a feeling that I did not know
          previously. I feel lightness and
          inner joy, amidst the struggle of

my life. Adorations to you,
teacher.

                    BESS
        Now go to sleep, for tomorrow will
        be a special day.

        You will meet the one who will
        show you love and passion's ways.

Heru laid down next to the fire as Bess hummed along. Then
Heru fell asleep.

                                        FADE OUT:

EXT. TEMPLE OF BES-DAWN

ON HERU'S FACE

Heru is asleep but the morning sun is now hitting his face,
becoming brighter and brighter. So much so that it wakes him
up. He turns to the sun and notices something peculiar about
it. He notices that Bess is not around.

                    HERU
        Lord Bess, Lord bess where are
        you?

Silence

                    HERU
        Why is the sun so bright and hot
        this morning? Bess, where are
        you?

Heru gets up and walks to the interior of the temple. In the
inner courtyard he notices a statue of a beautiful woman. He
walks up to it for a better look.

                    HERU
        And who might you be? Such beauty
        and perfection that radiate from
        this statue, who might you be in real life?

The sun begins to shine a powerful ray on the statue.
Suddenly, the statue moved slightly. This startled Heru and
he stepped back. Then he moved towards the statue to take a
closer look and it moved again. But this time a cracking
sound could be heard. Also, the ground began to tremble. A
ray of sunlight was shining on the statue and seemed to be
burning it.

                    HERU
        Praise be to Ra!

The pieces of stone were falling off and within was emerging
a woman of flesh and bone. The statue has now turned into the

most beautiful personality Heru could possible imagine.

Her golden brown skin glistens in the sunlight and her long black braided hair contrasts with the gold ornaments in it. On her head are the golden horns of a cow. She is dressed in a close fitting tunic that highlights her curvature.

>   HETHERU
>   Ahhhhhh... It is pleasing to be
>   in
>   human form again.

>   HERU
>   (amazed)
>   Who are you, lady of the statue,
>   and where do you come from?

Hetheru begins to walk towards Heru and then she circles him in a voluptuous manner.

>   HETHERU
>   My name is Hetheru and I am the
>   lady of fire. I am the sun
>   itself, the power of light. Who are you
>   if I may ask?

>   HERU
>   I am Heru, the son of Asar, the
>   lord of the black and Aset, the
>   mistress of wisdom and healing.

Hetheru takes Heru's hand.

>   HETHERU
>   Come with me, Heru, son of Asar
>   and Aset. I have something to
>   show
>   you.

>   HERU
>   Show me? But I must find my
>   teacher, Lord Bess.

>   HETHERU
>   Come with me, we will return
>   soon.

Heru leaves with her and they go into the wilderness. They come to a pond and find lotuses in the water. Hetheru takes one and begins to smell it.

>   HERU
>   Why have you brought me here dear
>   lady?

Hetheru placed the lotus in his hand and then moved it up towards his nose. It covered his whole face. He closed his

eyes and was taken with the fragrance. When he opened his
eyes she was gone.

>   HERU
>   Hetheru, where are you?

>   HETHERU (O.S.)
>   Here, here I am.

Heru turned in the direction of the sound and ran off.
Suddenly he found himself before a temple. He walked towards
it and saw Hetheru inside taking a bath. He watched her as
she moved gracefully within the water and soaped herself and
rinsed herself. He noticed how she enjoyed herself as if she
was supremely free. Then she came out and put on a see-
through garment. Like Aset's gown Hetheru wears a see-through
dress which exudes elegance and sensuous essence. The contour
of her voluptuous body is visible but there is no nudity, but
a sense of openness, peace and joy. Heru walked into her
chamber and began to speak.

>   HETHERU
>   Heru, Heru come and join me in
>   the pleasures of life.

Hetheru rubs ointments on her arms and legs.

>   HERU
>   Lady Hetheru, what pleasures do
>   you mean?

>   HETHERU
>   Life has many pleasures and you
>   have only learned precious few of
>   them in your short life. I on the
>   other hand have experienced the
>   all and today you will feel the
>   bliss of living.

>   HERU
>   Tell me, oh beautiful lady, what
>   is this bliss of which you speak?

>   HETHERU
>   Bliss is the flowering of the
>   soul. It is the harmony of life
>   and the flow of life's pure energy
>   through every part of your being.

>   HERU
>   I do not understand.

>   HETHERU
>   Tell me, young one, what does my
>   name mean to you?

>   HERU

151

Het means temple and heru
means...

          HETHERU
Yes, yes. Everything in this
universe has a counterpart and I
am yours. You live in me and I in
you. You are the sun and I am its
radiance. I am the Eye of Ra and the
power of Heru!

          HERU
Your words, I seem to hear for
the first time and yet it is as if I
have always known this same
truth.

The two embrace as if coming together after a long
separation.

          HERU
Tell me dearest one, why is it
that I did nor remember this
until now?

          HETHERU
Every being that takes human form
leaves behind a memory of the
past life. It is like falling asleep;
you forget who you are and then
the dream world becomes your
reality.

          HERU
But how is it possible to regain
this lost memory?

          HETHERU
Your memories are never lost. They
just go deep into your mind.
Sometimes the memory is a feeling
in your heart. At other times you
may recall an entire past life.
In time you will learn how to

discover them again and when you
do you will discover who you
really are deep down inside. This
is why I and everyone you know
have come into you life to teach
you these mysteries.

          HERU
I am remembering now, a feeling,
a kinship with you that I cannot
describe.

> HETHERU
>
> Yes, we have shared a love from
> the beginning of time you and I.
> I as the sun and you as the
> spirit. We both have been from
> the beginning of time and we shall
> ever be for all eternity.

Heru looks down as if remembering.

> HETHERU
>
> Beloved, you have come to this
> world at this time for a noble
> cause, to fight ignorance, anger,
> hatred and greed and to rid the
> earth of unrighteousness. First
> you must know the power of the
> sun, the power that is within your
> heart, and then you will have the
> strength for the struggle that is
> ahead for you.

> HERU
>
> How will I know this power?

> HETHERU
>
> I will show you. Give me your
> hand.

Hetheru takes Heru's hand with her left hand and picks up an
instrument with her right hand and begins to shake it. it is
a sistrum. A light appears in an adjacent room. Then she puts
the sistrum down and leads Heru to it.

> HETHERU
>
> We belong to each other, you and
> I. This world is our creation and
> it is ours to cherish.
>
> Come with me and we will discover
> the wonders of the inner light of
> the heart.

The two walk hand in hand towards an inner room. Within it
is the burning hot sun. They walk into it and disappear.

> FADE OUT:

EXT. TEMPLE OF BES-DAWN

Heru began to wake up, just as he had done before. Only,
this time, Bess was there in the same spot he (Bess) had seen

him

before he fell asleep the night before.

> HERU
>
> Bess, is that you?

153

Bess is smiling.

> HERU
> What happened? I woke up and met
> Hetheru and...

> BESS
> You discovered your love!

> HERU
> Yes, yes. But where is she now?

> BESS
> Where she always has been, in
> your heart!

> HERU
> Yes, yes indeed.

> BESS
> Heru, the time has come for you to
> leave. The moment for which you
> have prepared, is coming soon.
> Your uncle, Set is at this very
> moment preparing to force the
> court of Anu, the highest in the
> land, to proclaim him as the king
> of Egypt. Without anyone to oppose
> him they will have no choice but
> to agree.

> HERU
> But dear master, how will I reach
> there in time, it is a two day
> journey?

> BESS
> Never fear, my son, for the
> righteous there is always a means
> to success. You now have the power
> to fly. Search your inner self for
> the memory of the Hawk. Recall the
> vision of your father in his form
> as Sokar. You to have the power of
> the Hawk. Look within yourself and
> you will see.

ON HERU'S LEFT EYE

Suddenly the eye turned into a brightly colored eye of a
hawk.

> BESS
> Look deeper and find your wings!
> Believe, in yourself, believe in

yourself and you can fly! You can
Fly!

Suddenly, Heru's head transformed into a hawk's head. Then his body transformed into a hawk and he took flight. Bess spread out his arms and began to dance as a child who pretends to fly while running around in circles.

> BESS
> Before you reach your final
> destination, stop and pay homage
> to the human headed lion an ask
> for its blessing. Fly my son, fly
> and rescue this land from the
> evil of Set.

> HERU
> I will, I will...

EXT. GIZA PLATEAU THE SPINX-DAY

Heru reached the Giza plateau where the imposing figure of the Sphinx is located. He flew downward and landed between its legs and then turned into his human form. He kneeled down on his right knee and began to pray to the sphinx.

> HERU
> Oh, silent one of ancient days,
> who looks eternally into the
> eastern horizon welcoming the
> sun.
> Bless me with tenacity, self-
> control, wisdom and faith so that
> I might meet the challenge ahead.
> Allow me to share in thy majesty,
> thy fortitude and steadfastness.

Heru stands up and surveys the majesty of the Sphinx and the pyramids. Then he faces the morning sun.

> HERU
> I vow on this day that I will do
> all that is in my power to bring
> back peace and justice to this
> land. Adorations to you Ra,
> Adorations to you Asar,
> Adorations to you Aset,
> Adorations to you Bess and my
> beloved Hetheru. May your power be
> with me in this struggle and may
> I never disappoint you.

ONE RIGHT EYE OF HERU, FADE INTO THE REFLECTION OF THE GOLDEN SUN

> CUT TO:

INT. THRONE ROOM, CITY OF ANU - DAY

Set is at the city of Anu, talking with a servant

          SET
Send a message to the court. I
want to meet the court of Ra and
have it proclaim me as the King
or Egypt. Tell them that I expect a
swift ruling.

          SERVANT
Yes my lord, at once my lord.

          SET
       (to himself)
Now that the weak child Heru is
dead, I want everyone to proclaim
me as the only king of this great
land. No one can stop me now. I
have the world in my hand.

          SERVANT
You will be admitted now lord
Set.

          SET
Well it's about time!

Set walks into a great hall of the palace where the great
gods an goddesses meet. The interior walls and floors are
studded with gold and precious jewels of all kinds. Forty two
gods and goddesses sit along the sides of the hall and in the
furthermost part sit the great gods and goddesses Geb and Nut
on One side and Shu and Tefnut on the other. In the center is
the throne. On it sits Ra. Before him stand Maat, Djehuti and
Hetheru. Aset is also present. She is seated next to her
parents, Geb and Nut.

          DJEHUTI
Who has business at this great
court. Come forward now and plead
your case.

Set struts in smugly.

          SET
I have business with this court.

          DJEHUTI
State your name and plead your
case.

          SET
You know who I am. I am Set. From
the beginning of time you have all
known me as the servant of Ra, as
the protector of his barque of

millions of years. Now I demand my
rewards for the service which I
have provided for so long. I
demand to be proclaimed as the
lord of the land of Egypt!

        DJEHUTI
On what basis do you make this
claim? Was there not already a
king of Egypt?

        SET
          (angrily)
I do not want to speak to you. I
demand to address Ra directly!

        DJEHUTI
Why do you turn away from me? Do
you fear the truth?

        SET
          (angrily)
I will tell you the truth. Only
the strong and proud deserve to be
kings and queens. I am strong and
proud and fearless, therefore I am
worthy to be king! None of you can
oppose me. I am the rightful heir
to the throne. There is no other
person who can challenge me.

Right after Set uttered those words of defiance the doors to
the hall began to open. All who were present turned to see
who it was. Standing just outside was Heru.

        RA
Who is that hansom figure at the
door?

        HETHERU
          (smiling, full of
          glee)
It is Heru, my lord. It is my
Heru!

Heru walks in proudly and stands in front of the court, next
to Set and looks at him.

        HERU
I will challenge you!

        SET
And who are you anyway? What
business do you have here? These
are royal matters that do not
concern a mere child. Leave at

once and cease disturbing us.

          HERU
I am Heru, the son of Asar, the
king of Egypt and Aset, the queen.
You are responsible for my
father's death. You imprisoned my
mother and it was also you who
sent an evil scorpion to kill me.

Set was surprised.

          SET
What lies do you speak?

          SHU
Is this true? Is this true?

          HERU
It is true on my honor, I swear it
is true, I swear by Maat!

          SHU
If this is true the throne
rightfully belongs to Heru no
matter how mighty Set might be.
Justice requires that Heru be
given the throne.

Djehuti agreed with Shu.

          DJEHUTI
What Shu has said is a million
times true!

          SHU
If everyone is in agreement about
this, let us proclaim Heru as the
king.

Then Set moved forward and shouted:

          SET
How can this puny child claim the
throne. He is a liar!

          DJEHUTI
What Set says is wrong; we all
know this. How can the throne be
given to Set when the rightful
heir is alive, right here before
us? Heru should be given the
throne. Are we not all in
agreement with that?

A strange silence came over the court. They all looked at
each other and then finally at Ra, the high one, for his

decree. The sun god, Ra, then said:

> RA
> I am not in agreement with that.

Having heard this, the entire hall fell into a cold silence. They were all in disbelief. Djehuti turned to Ra.

> DJEHUTI
> Sire, I do not understand. The
> answer to this issue seems clear.

> RA
> I have my reasons. I am not in
> agreement with this hasty
> judgement of the court.

The gods and goddesses looked at each other, wondering what to do next. Then Set spoke again.

> SET
> The throne belongs to me. Who else
> but me protects the voyage of the
> sun boat when the chaos serpents
> attack it? Since I am the one who
> protects the existence of the gods
> and goddesses and all creation,
> the throne should be given to me!

> DJEHUTI
> We cannot give the throne to an
> uncle when the rightful heir is
> standing right here before us!

> HERU
> Will you take away my birthright
> with this injustice and do it
> right here in front of the highest
> court of gods and goddesses?

Hearing all of this, Aset, who was sitting nearby, became exceedingly angry and complained incessantly at the apparent wavering of the court.

> ASET
> I am Aset, the goddess of wisdom
> and truth. I stand before you, as
> a widow because of what Set has
> done! I was imprisoned and then
> faced the illness of my son! All
> of these calamities are the doing
> of the greedy one who stands
> before you! If you do not grant
> the throne to it's rightful heir
> you cannot claim to be a court of
> justice and Maat will turn away
> from you because you will be

against Maat!

Noticing that the court was not supporting him, Set now became furious and threatened them all:

> SET
> From now on, anyone who is against me, I will strike every single day, and furthermore I will not put forth my case in any court where Aset is allowed to enter. If you want to decide who should be the king let him challenge me to a contest of strength, a duel it should be!

With complete confidence, Heru agreed immediately to the challenge.

> HERU
> I accept your challenge. Fight you, I will. For what is true must be upheld, lest the universe should crumble into chaos and decay and the home of humanity be lost.

FOCUS ON RA'S FACE

Ra smiled and nodded with approval when he heard this.

> RA
> (standing up and lifting his arm to address all who were present)
> Then begin the contest at once.

On hearing all of this, Aset began to weep, because she feared that Set would kill her son. Nut consoled her.

> ASET
> (sobbing)
> Oh, calamity of calamities! My son will fight the evil one and he is so young still!

> NUT
> Fear not my daughter, Heru has a great heart and also the favor of Maat. His virtue will see him through the challenges that lie ahead.

EXT. NILE RIVER-BATTLE SCENE - DAY

The entire court appeared at the banks of the Nile river.

                DJEHUTI
            (addressing Set and
            Heru)
Now listen, this contest will
decide the future of the world.
The victor among you will lead
the world. Therefore, let this
momentous contest begin.

                SET
            (turning into is
            demonic form)
Now you will be destroyed, foolish
child. You should never have
challenged me. Poor Aset, she has
lost her husband and now she will
lose her son too.

                HERU
            (angrily)
You are the cause of my father's
death and now you will pay for your
unrighteousness!

Suddenly, swords appear in the two combatants hands and they
begin to fight. The sound of their clashing is like thunder.
When the swords touch, lightning flashes. When ever they miss
and hit a stone or a tree that object explodes. The fierce
battle rages as one seems to gain the upper hand over the
other and then loses the advantage. In a tight clinch Set
speaks to Heru.

                SET
            (with angry arrogance)
Your efforts are useless against
me. You cannot win this fight. You
do not have the power to resist
me. Give up now and I will spare
you.

                HERU
            (determined)
Save your evil speech, Set, who
will listen to the sound of lies
and greed.

                SET
            (smirking)
What is the matter little one, are
you having doubts?

Set drops his sword and transforms into a hippopotamus. Heru
looks on with amazement.

                    SET
               (continuing)
          Let us see if you have enough
          courage to follow me.

Set runs towards the Nile and submerges beneath the surface.

Heru dropped his sword and transformed himself into a
hippopotamus and followed him in. Set turned around
traitorously and struck Heru. They began to fight. Even the
crocodiles were afraid and they left the river and sought
safety elsewhere. The struggle went on and at one point they
came on shore and continued fighting. As they shoved each
other into buildings and trees which collapsed and toppled
over and their power was tested but neither could overpower
the other. Their power was extraordinary, as their blows were
heard throughout the land. Shu walked up to Ra and Djehuti.

                    SHU
          The two combatants are equal in
          strength. How will we decide who
          is to be the king?

They did not answer Shu but continued looking at the combat
intently.

Then Set stepped away from Heru and looked at him strangely.
Heru paused for a moment and the world began to dissolve and
spin.

                    SET
               (smirking)
          What's the matter Heru, losing
          grip on the world.

                    HERU
               (feeling dizzy)
          What, what is happening to me?

Heru turned towards the spectators and they faded from his
view.

                    HERU
               (continuing)
          Where are you going. Don't leave
          me. I can't do it alone. Please.

                    SET
          What is the matter little one.
          Feeling all alone and lost? I will
          show you the true meaning of
          power. You should never have
          challenged me!

Heru fell to his knees. Set turned his free hand into a half
canine, half leonine metal claw, moved forward and scratched
the defenseless Heru's eyes.

GEB
Look at what Set has done. He has
taken an unfair advantage and
injured Heru!

The world suddenly reappeared as it was. Heru fell, screaming
in pain, to the ground, now blind and in pain. Set moved to
finish him off but suddenly someone stood in his way. It was
Djehuti.

DJEHUTI
Will you now compound lies with
murder once more and in front of
the court?

SET
Stand aside or you will join Heru
in death!

Djehuti did not move so Set, who was beside himself, lunged
at him. But it had no effect. Djehuti was protected by the
light of Ra and could not be harmed. As Set knocked into
Djehuti he was repulsed as if by a stronger force, an aura of
light emanating from Ra's forehead. Djehuti did not even
move. Djehuti began to transformed himself into his real
transcendental form, a body of a man with the head of an Ibis
bird wearing a double plumed headdress and in doing so
distracted Set. Djehuti grabbed Set and blocked his view by
spreading his wings over him. This gave Heru a chance to
escape. Heru ran as he held his face and blood could be seen
coming from the region of his eyes. After running away for
some time he found a place to sit which was out of sight. He
began to weep. Hetheru went to him.

HETHERU
Oh dear one of my heart, where are
you, let me help you.

HERU
I am blind, I cannot see what is
before me. Go away, I do not want
you to see me like this.

HETHERU
(kneeling beside him
with compassion)
Oh, Dear one, do not be concerned
with pride or embarrassment.

Everyone needs the help of friends
and I love you as my very self.
Come, I will take you to a place
of safety.

Hetheru took Heru's hand and they began to walk and
disappeared. When they reappear she led him to a secluded
place in the mountains. There she consoled him and nursed
him. She found a gazelle and took some of its milk in her
hand and as she looked at it, a golden serpent emanated from
her forehead. It opened its mouth and a golden beam came
forth and went into the milk, making it glow a golden glow.
Then she took it to Heru. She spoke to him with the lovely
sound of a celestial melody:

> HETHERU
> (continuing)
> Uncover your eyes Heru my love. I
> have brought you a healing
> preparation to restore your vision.

Heru did as he was told, and she dripped the milk which was
imbued with light energy. His eyes began to glow and his
strength was restored but he could still not see.

> HERU
> (disheartened)
> I have failed, I failed in my
> duty.

> HETHERU
> What do you mean?

> HERU
> I failed to restore Maat. I did
> not defeat Set.

> HETHERU
> Dearest one, reflect on what you
> know and you will see that you are
> thinking wrongly.

> HERU
> Wrongly? How am I wrong? Look at
> me. I am injured and I have left
> the battle. Has not Set beaten me?
> Didn't Ra side with him against me
> when we pleaded our case?

> HETHERU
> Beaten you? Far from it I should
> think.
>
> No one has stood up to Set as you
> did. He is treacherous and
> uncaring and selfish. You are
> noble because you fight for what
> is true. Remember the lesson you
> learned from Bess. You trusted him
> to fight fairly and then you did

not watch him closely. This is why
he injured you.

HERU
No! I am unworthy.

HETHERU
Heru, my darling, I can heal your
eyes and bring you the strength of
the sun itself but you must heal
your heart. You are the purest of
the pure, the noblest of the
noble. This is why you are hurting
so deeply now and it is also why
you must fight on till the end.

HERU
What you say may be true, but how
will I carry forth the fight from
here on? I have used all of the
weapons that I know and yet I
cannot overcome Set.

HETHERU
(with determination)
Your victory is in not giving in.
No matter how bad the conditions
may be, you must never give in to
evil and deceit. This is your
mission, to show the world that
Maat endures even when the world
is full of tyrants and
unrighteousness. Do not give into
fear or hopelessness. That is the
way to failure. Trust in Maat and
her philosophy and even if your
body is destroyed, you will still
be victorious in the end. For it
is said: "Those who live today
will die tomorrow, those who die
tomorrow will be born again; Those
who live Maat will not die."

HERU
Yes! What you say is true.

HETHERU
Unrighteousness never lasts, no
matter how powerful it may seem to
be. It cannot last because it is
not based on truth. Only love and
peace and harmony can last and
endure because they are eternal
gifts of Ra. Hate and fear are the
fruits of ignorance and weakness.

Do not give into Set's taunting.
This will distract you from your
goal. Do not give into the hatred
of Set and always have faith that
Ra in his wisdom will support you
in your struggle to free the world.

                    HERU
                (smiling)
I can see your face now, a most
beautiful sight. But I am still
uncertain as to the path that I
must take.

A silence comes over them as Hetheru moves towards Heru and
hugs him. Suddenly, a soft noise breaks the silence and a
subtle light appears nearby.

                    HERU
                (continuing)
What is that strange light?

Before Hetheru can answer the light takes shape.

                    HETHERU
It is Lord Djehuti.

Heru immediately prostrates before Lord Djehuti.

                    HERU
Oh, great sir, thank you for
saving me from Set.

                    DJEHUTI
                (placing his right
                 hand on Heru's head)
There is no time for praises my
son. Set will not be fooled by the
illusion that I am holding him
back at the banks of the Nile.

                    HERU
You mean you are not holding him?

                    DJEHUTI
No one can hold Set back in his
wrath except Set himself. Listen
to me carefully. Set's strength
comes from his anger and egoistic
desire. Therefore it is limited
and this limitation will bring his
downfall. Your strength comes from
a place much higher, where there
is infinite, and boundless power.
You must look within yourself and
fully discover it.

Djehuti lifts his hand up and immediately they are both
transported to the surface of the moon.

               HERU
Where are we now?

               DJEHUTI
This is the moon, my special
abode. Here in absolute peace and
silence you will hear the greatest
teaching of life. This teaching
will give you the fortitude to
succeed in your challenge.

               HERU
Speak on great sir, I offer myself
as your devoted student.

               DJEHUTI
Look up and tell me what you see.

               HERU
I see the blackness of space and
the glory of countless stars in
the body of grandmother Nut.

               DJEHUTI
And what else?

               HERU
I see, I see the sun in his glory,
singular, powerful and true.

               DJEHUTI
And...Look deeply into the sun and
tell me what you see.

               HERU
I see, I see the great boat of Ra,
journeying from the beginning of
time. I see Ra in his boat with
Maat before him.

               DJEHUTI
Now look at Ra closely.

               HERU
I see, I see...

               DJEHUTI
Focus on Ra, Focus!

               HERU
I see, it is not possible!

               DJEHUTI
Yes!

                    HERU
It is me, but...

                    DJEHUTI
Yes it is you. You are one with Ra
and in this truth is your strength.

                    HERU
But if I am one with Ra why did he
send me...

                    DJEHUTI
The soul of every living thing is
Ra, my son. They have all been
sent to the world so that they may
learn and grow and discover the
glory of Ra within themselves.
This is the struggle of life of
good against evil, right against
wrong. Anyone who realizes this
discovers the power and glory of
Ra and can do great things. They
can defeat any evil force.

                    HERU
I have so many questions that have
plagued my heart and weakened my
resolve. Why did Ra allow Set to
kill Asar and steal the throne of
Egypt? Why did Ra help Set against
me? How did Set dissolve the world
from my view on the battle field?

                    DJEHUTI
 Ra, in his wisdom was behind the
entire affair. His apparent help
to Set was in reality a help to
you and the world. To bring on
this conflict so that you might
become stronger because of it and
so that it may serve as an example
for generations to come. Behold,
Asar is not dead but the righteous
King of those in the Netherworld.

Asar appears from the darkness turning into a shining figure.

                    HERU
Father, I missed you.

                    ASAR
Oh my son, I am so proud of you,
what you have become and are
becoming. To the wise Lord Djehuti
you must listen and heed, for this
is the greatest hour, for which we

have all prepared.

           DJEHUTI
Oh worthy one, valiant champion of
truth and righteousness, listen
carefully and with an open heart
to my words of wisdom. The
physical world and the Netherworld
are Ra's creation for the
schooling of souls. They are not
real and therefore nothing that
happens there can hurt you or
anyone who realizes this great
truth. Your true being is like the
sun, indestructible and pure and
your body is only a reflection of
your true being.

           HERU
You mean that I am not really
here? I cannot be killed?

           DJEHUTI
Are you there in your dream when
you sleep? Can you die in a dream?

           HERU
No, it is only a dream.

           DJEHUTI
And these worlds are Ra's dreams,
your dreams. Nobody dies here,
they only learn by the grace of
Maat, who punishes unrighteous
deeds and rewards the righteous
ones and then they move on to a
new life. Set caused a delusion in
your mind because you doubted the
truth. Doubt and fear make you
vulnerable to anger and hatred and
ignorance of your own making or
that of others. If you are strong
in truth you can control the world
with your mind and the power of
your true words.

           HERU
True words?

           DJEHUTI
Yes, this is what we call
Maakheru. All who live a righteous
life discover the gift of true
speech. All who speak truth have
the power of true speech and this
enables them to do great things.
By your great example, countless

generations will learn the path to
Nehast, spiritual enlightenment.

            HERU
I will show the way?

            DJEHUTI
 Yes. Therefore, if you want to
succeed in your challenge against
Set and lead the world to harmony
and prosperity you must live by
truth. This means you must lose
all doubts and illusions about the
world and who you are.

            HERU
What do you mean, by doubts and
illusions?

            DJEHUTI
You have received teachings from
your mother, the goddess of wisdom
herself, from the great lord Bess
and from goddess Hetheru, the
mistress of power and yet you do
not truly believe that you have
the knowledge and power to defeat
Set.

            HERU
But every move I make is countered
and I can't stop him.

            DJEHUTI
But? Can't? These are not words
used by those who see Ra in their
heart! Listen young king to be,
listen carefully. You are one with
Ra. There is no greater force than
he. Use his power to vanquish your
enemy.

            HERU
How? Tell me master.

            DJEHUTI
Every atom in the universe has
Sekhem, the power to create or to
destroy. Set's power comes from
his ego and thus it is limited to
his anger and hatred. You must go
deeper and discover the power of
Ra within you.

            HERU
How can I access this Sekhem power?

DJEHUTI
First you must not only believe
that you are one with Ra you must
feel him in every cell of your
being. Then utter the special
elemental words of power so you
can use the world as your ally.

HERU
The world is my ally?

DJEHUTI
Yes, of course. Was it not said
that in the beginning Ra created
his son Shu the air and his
daughter Tefnut, the water and
their son and daughter Geb, the
earth and Nut the Sky?

HERU
Yes, yes.

DJEHUTI
Whenever you utter these names
with faith and true willing you
will have their power, they will
help you in the struggle.

HERU
You mean...

DJEHUTI
Yes, the ultimate power of the
universe is yours if you are true
and if you believe in your Self!

HERU
 But what about Set? Can't he get
this power too?

DJEHUTI
Set cannot realize this truth
because his mind is clouded with
anger, hatred and greed. It is
only for the pure of heart alone,
the righteous because only they
can experience Hetep, peace and
this leads them to clarity and truth.

HERU
(closing his eyes and
then opening in
amazement)
Oh great sir, I feel a great power
coursing through me. It is deep
inside but also everywhere I look.

When Heru opens his eyes everything is permeated by an aura.

                    DJEHUTI
          Yes, the life force is everywhere
          and with your mind you must feel
          it and with it you can feel
          everything in Creation, no matter
          how far away. Feel the land.

Heru lifts his arm and then the ground begins to move.

                    HERU
               (exited)
          Geb, I, feel it!

                    DJEHUTI
          Now see that boulder over there,
          lift it up.

                    HERU
          It is so large, are you shure...

                    DJEHUTI
          Do not speak, lift with your heart!

Heru motions with his arm and lifts the boulder and smiles
and then sets it down. Heru looks at his hands, then at
Djehuti.

                    DJEHUTI
               (continuing)
          Now do you understand the power
          and glory of truth?

                    HERU
               (with resolve)
          Yes uncle. The power and the glory
          of truth.

                    DJEHUTI
          There is one more thing, Oh
          champion of truth. Do not attempt
          to kill Set. Killing is against
          Maat and it leads to more unrest
          and evil. Instead, frustrate him
          and counter every move that he
          makes until he gives in and turns
          away from evil. You must endure
          and outlast him. When you are free
          of hatred and guilt and sorrow you
          will commune with the highest
          power that is within you. If you
          do this, you will have invincible
          power!

                    HERU
          I will heed your words great

master.

                    DJEHUTI
This is the most important
teaching. Never forget you are one
with God. Never forget you are not
a weakling but powerful and strong
in Ra! You are Heru, the son of
Asar and Aset, the spirit of Ra
who encompasses all!

                    HERU
            (with conviction)
I am Heru!... I have the Power! I
have the Power!

Heru suddenly reappeared back with Hetheru. He stood up with
renewed confidence and understanding and clenched his fists.
He holds Hetheru's shoulders and speaks to her with
tenderness.

                    HERU
            (continuing)
Hetheru, through your words and
healing power I can see a path
now. I am renewed and transformed
in body and mind due to your care
and nurturing. Whatever may happen
now, I will always remember this.
Neither I nor the world will ever
forget what you have done for me
on this day of my greatest need.
I will now face Set again.

                    HETHERU
            (with upraised arms)
Oh great one, lord of the
universe, I salute you and pay
homage to you. May you glorify
this world with your presence and
may all follow in your steps my
lord.

He turned to return to the battlefield where Set and the
court were gathered.

                    ASET
            (relieved)
Look, look, the child of Asar
returns!

This time he looked more noble, powerful and determined. Ra looked on with approval as Heru returned to the battlefield.

>   SET
>   (taunting and
>   threatening)
>   Well, the child has returned. Now
>   I will finish you for good and I
>   will claim my prize, the land of
>   light will be mine finally!

>   HERU
>   I stand here before you as a
>   warrior but not for myself. I
>   fight for the sake of
>   righteousness and justice. You
>   will never defeat these principles
>   because they are eternal and pure.

The two combatants went at it again. This time they constructed boats and battled each other from these, throwing exploding spears and then thunder bolt arrows back and forth. Djehuti consulted Ra about this seemingly endless matter.

>   DJEHUTI
>   Sire, the contest between the two
>   combatants rages on without a
>   resolution. What shall we do?

>   RA
>   I am aware of the situation and I
>   declare to all in the court, that
>   I am prepared to see this matter
>   through to the end.

Set became frustrated and lunged at Heru in his wrathful form. His attack was easily repelled by Heru. Once again, this was pleasing to Ra, who was looking on.

>   HERU
>   Set! Retreat from the path of
>   unrighteousness. Turn away from
>   lies and deceit and accept the
>   ways of Maat!

>   SET
>   Do not lecture me on philosophy.
>   You are a mere child and I will
>   finish you now.

Set lifted his arm and in his had appeared a mace. He threw it at Heru but a golden light flashed from Heru's forehead and disintegrated it. Next Set began to through a series of objects at Heru.

First, a tree was uprooted and hurled at Heru, then a boulder and then great wall of water arose from the Nile river like

a storm. A golden disk emerged from Heru's forehead which he
took and used as a shield which deflected the objects. Next,
Set began to yell with such loudness that all except Ra and
Heru had to hold their ears. Set bent back and then leaned
forward and let out a great fireball from his mouth towards
Heru.

> NEBETHET
> (scared)
> Oh no, what will Heru do now?

Closing his eyes and placing his arms in a cross on his
chest he created an aura that the fireball could not
penetrate. When the smoke cleared the figure of Heru was
visible again, now it was shining a golden glow. Heru opened
eyes and emanated a blinding light. Then Heru opened his arms
and from them emerged wings. He began to transform into a
giant Hawk. He began to unfurl his wings.

> SET
> (angrily)
> You foolish child, you cannot
> defeat me with your magical tricks.

Set lunged at Heru and with a single bound from 50 feet away
tried to ram into him. Heru flapped his wings in such a way
that a strong wind developed which engulfed Set and threw him
into the Nile. When he emerged he was amazed because he had
to look straight up in order to see Heru's head. Heru had
spread his wings and his wingspan was so large that Set could
not see one end to the other.

> SET
> (continuing)
> No! No, it cannot be. No!

Everything became permeated with the golden glow of Heru's
body. Set fell to his knees at the river's edge and began to
weep. He knew he was defeated and the entire court knew it as
well. Ra stood up and his head transformed itself into a hawk
head like Heru's and his crown became the sun itself, which
came down from the sky and rested on his head. Then he began
to speak.

> RA
> On this day, which will be
> remembered for all time, I
> proclaim Heru as King of Egypt.
> Set, my son, you have learned the
> lesson of humility and truth.
>
> For I said long ago that "Maat is
> great and its effectiveness
> lasting; it has not been disturbed

176

since the time of Asar. There is
punishment for those who pass over
it's laws, but this is unfamiliar
to the covetous one....When the
end is near, Maat lasts."

                SET
            (looking down in
             shame)
I accept your decree and place
myself at your mercy.

                RA
This is my command for you. Return
back to the barque of millions of
years and protect it as you have
done since the beginning of time.
When you discover the glory of
service you will, in time, also
have the riches of joy and
pleasure as your heart may then
desire.

                SET
Praise be to you, monarch
everlasting. Merciful and
compassionate are your words and
plans. I accept this decree
without resentment or regret and
vow to fulfill my duty until the
end of time.

Heru returns to his human form and is adored by all the gods
and goddesses with upraised arms. Aset began to shout with
joy.

            GODS AND GODDESSES
Dua Heru! Dua Heru! Dua Heru!
Dua Heru!

                ASET
Hail to the son of Asar! Hail to
the light of the world!

 Asar and all the gods and goddesses and the souls of the
departed in the kingdom of the dead dropped their work and
turned their attention towards Heru and also rejoiced.
Djehuti now began to speak.

                DJEHUTI
This certainly is a most
auspicious day. We have witnessed
the form of Heru as the all-
encompassing wings which are
invincible. As a sign for all who
will come in the future, I decree
that a symbol of this form be

177

placed above the entrance to our
temples as a sign of protection
and strength from evil and
unrighteousness. Hail Heru-Ur!

                    CROWD
               (rejoicing)
          Dua Heru-Ur! Dua Heru-Ur! Dua Heru-
          Ur! Hail Heru-Ur! Hail the Great
          One!

The gods and goddesses praised Djehuti's words. Heru smiles
as he is congratulated and praised by all. He then walks over
to his mother, kisses her feet and then hugs her. As he
raises his eyes Asar appears in spirit form also smiling
proudly.

ON HERU'S SMILING FACE

                                        FADE OUT:

INT. THRONE ROOM, CITY OF ABDU - DAY

Heru sits on the throne in full raiment as king of all Egypt.
Aset and Nebethet are standing on one side of him and Hetheru
is standing on the other alongside the goddess Maat. There is
a multitude both outside and inside of the palace. They are
all listening to the words of Djehuti.

                    DJEHUTI
          On this day I proclaim that
          righteousness has returned to the
          land.

                    CROWD
          Cheers of joy.

                    DJEHUTI
          I further declare that Heru, the
          son of king Asar and queen
          Aset is now the king of Egypt.

                    CROWD
          Dua Heru, Neb Tawi! Dua Heru, Neb
          Tawi! Adorations to Heru, the Lord
          of the two lands.

Djehuti places the double crown of Egypt (white and red) on
Heru's head, officially marking his coronation.

                    CROWD
               (continuing)
          More cheers

All the people cheered, danced and sang in the streets on
learning of the coronation of Heru. Then the crowd within the

throne room begins a chant in adoration of the king and his family.

                    CROWD
              (continuing)
         Om Asar Aset Heru...
         Om Asar Aset Heru...
         Om Asar Aset Heru...
         Om Asar Aset Heru...
         Om Asar Aset Heru...

                              FADE OUT:

OUTER SPACE

END CREDITS

                    THE END

General Index

Other Books From C M Books

P.O.Box 570459
Miami, Florida, 33257
(305) 378-6253 Fax: (305) 378-6253

This book is part of a series on the study and practice of Ancient Egyptian Yoga and Mystical Spirituality based on the writings of Dr. Muata Abhaya Ashby. They are also part of the Egyptian Yoga Course provided by the Sema Institute of Yoga. Below you will find a listing of the other books in this series. For more information send for the Egyptian Yoga Book-Audio-Video Catalog or the Egyptian Yoga Course Catalog.

Now you can study the teachings of Egyptian and Indian Yoga wisdom and Spirituality with the Egyptian Yoga Mystical Spirituality Series. The Egyptian Yoga Series takes you through the Initiation process and lead you to understand the mysteries of the soul and the Divine and to attain the highest goal of life: ENLIGHTENMENT. The *Egyptian Yoga Series*, takes you on an in depth study of Ancient Egyptian mythology and their inner mystical meaning. Each Book is prepared for the serious student of the mystical sciences and provides a study of the teachings along with exercises, assignments and projects to make the teachings understood and effective in real life. The Series is part of the Egyptian Yoga course but may be purchased even if you are not taking the course. The series is ideal for study groups.

Prices subject to change.

1. EGYPTIAN YOGA: THE PHILOSOPHY OF ENLIGHTENMENT An original, fully illustrated work, including hieroglyphs, detailing the meaning of the Egyptian mysteries, tantric yoga, psycho-spiritual and physical exercises. Egyptian Yoga is a guide to the practice of the highest spiritual philosophy which leads to absolute freedom from human misery and to immortality. It is well known by scholars that Egyptian philosophy is the basis of Western and Middle Eastern religious philosophies such as *Christianity, Islam, Judaism,* the *Kabala*, and Greek philosophy, but what about Indian philosophy, Yoga and Taoism? What were the original teachings? How can they be practiced today? What is the source of pain and suffering in the world and what is the solution? Discover the deepest mysteries of the mind and universe within and outside of your self. 8.5" X 11" ISBN: 1-884564-01-1 Soft $19.95

2. EGYPTIAN YOGA II: The Supreme Wisdom of Enlightenment by Dr. Muata Ashby ISBN 1-884564-39-9 $23.95 U.S. In this long awaited sequel to *Egyptian Yoga: The Philosophy of Enlightenment* you will take a fascinating and enlightening journey back in time and discover the teachings which constituted the epitome of Ancient Egyptian spiritual wisdom. What are the disciplines which lead to the fulfillment of all desires? Delve into the three states of consciousness (waking, dream and deep sleep) and the fourth state which transcends them all, Neberdjer, "The Absolute." These teachings of the city of Waset (Thebes) were the crowning achievement of the Sages of Ancient Egypt. They establish the standard mystical keys for understanding the profound mystical symbolism of the Triad of human consciousness.

3. THE KEMETIC DIET: GUIDE TO HEALTH, DIET AND FASTING Health issues have always been important to human beings since the beginning of time. The earliest records of history show that the art of healing was held in high esteem since the time of Ancient Egypt. In the early 20th century, medical doctors had almost attained the status of sainthood by the promotion of the idea that they alone were "scientists" while other healing modalities and traditional healers who did not follow the "scientific method' were nothing but superstitious, ignorant charlatans who at best would take the money of their clients and at worst kill them with the unscientific "snake oils" and "irrational theories". In the late 20th century, the failure of the modern medical establishment's ability to lead the general public to good health, promoted the move by many in society towards "alternative medicine". Alternative medicine disciplines are those healing modalities which do not adhere to the philosophy of allopathic medicine. Allopathic medicine is what medical doctors practice by an large. It is the theory that disease is caused by agencies outside the body such as bacteria, viruses or physical means which affect the body. These can therefore be treated by medicines and therapies The natural healing method began in the absence of extensive technologies with

the idea that all the answers for health may be found in nature or rather, the deviation from nature. Therefore, the health of the body can be restored by correcting the aberration and thereby restoring balance. This is the area that will be covered in this volume. Allopathic techniques have their place in the art of healing. However, we should not forget that the body is a grand achievement of the spirit and built into it is the capacity to maintain itself and heal itself. Ashby, Muata ISBN: 1-884564-49-6 $28.95

4.   INITIATION INTO EGYPTIAN YOGA Shedy: Spiritual discipline or program, to go deeply into the mysteries, to study the mystery teachings and literature profoundly, to penetrate the mysteries. You will learn about the mysteries of initiation into the teachings and practice of Yoga and how to become an Initiate of the mystical sciences. This insightful manual is the first in a series which introduces you to the goals of daily spiritual and yoga practices: Meditation, Diet, Words of Power and the ancient wisdom teachings. 8.5" X 11" ISBN 1-884564-02-X   Soft Cover $24.95 U.S.

5.   *THE AFRICAN ORIGINS OF CIVILIZATION, MYSTICAL RELIGION AND YOGA PHILOSOPHY* HARD COVER EDITION ISBN: 1-884564-50-X $80.00 U.S.   81/2" X 11"   Part 1, Part 2, Part 3 in one volume 683 Pages Hard Cover First Edition Three volumes in one. Over the past several years I have been asked to put together in one volume the most important evidences showing the correlations and common teachings between Kamitan (Ancient Egyptian) culture and religion and that of India. The questions of the history of Ancient Egypt, and the latest archeological evidences showing civilization and culture in Ancient Egypt and its spread to other countries, has intrigued many scholars as well as mystics over the years. Also, the possibility that Ancient Egyptian Priests and Priestesses migrated to Greece, India and other countries to carry on the traditions of the Ancient Egyptian Mysteries, has been speculated over the years as well. In chapter 1 of the book *Egyptian Yoga The Philosophy of Enlightenment,* 1995, I first introduced the deepest comparison between Ancient Egypt and India that had been brought forth up to that time. Now, in the year 2001 this new book, *THE AFRICAN ORIGINS OF CIVILIZATION, MYSTICAL RELIGION AND YOGA PHILOSOPHY,* more fully explores the motifs, symbols and philosophical correlations between Ancient Egyptian and Indian mysticism and clearly shows not only that Ancient Egypt and India were connected culturally but also spiritually. How does this knowledge help the spiritual aspirant? This discovery has great importance for the Yogis and mystics who follow the philosophy of Ancient Egypt and the mysticism of India. It means that India has a longer history and heritage than was previously understood. It shows that the mysteries of Ancient Egypt were essentially a yoga tradition which did not die but rather developed into the modern day systems of Yoga technology of India. It further shows that African culture developed Yoga Mysticism earlier than any other civilization in history. All of this expands our understanding of the unity of culture and the deep legacy of Yoga, which stretches into the distant past, beyond the Indus Valley civilization, the earliest known high culture in India as well as the Vedic tradition of Aryan culture. Therefore, Yoga culture and mysticism is the oldest known tradition of spiritual development and Indian mysticism is an extension of the Ancient Egyptian mysticism. By understanding the legacy which Ancient Egypt gave to India the mysticism of India is better understood and by comprehending the heritage of Indian Yoga, which is rooted in Ancient Egypt the Mysticism of Ancient Egypt is also better understood. This expanded understanding allows us to prove the underlying kinship of humanity, through the common symbols, motifs and philosophies which are not disparate and confusing teachings but in reality expressions of the same study of truth through metaphysics and mystical realization of Self. (HARD COVER)

6.   AFRICAN ORIGINS BOOK 1 PART 1 African Origins of African Civilization, Religion, Yoga Mysticism and Ethics Philosophy-<u>Soft Cover</u> $24.95 ISBN: 1-884564-55-0

7.   AFRICAN ORIGINS BOOK 2 PART 2 African Origins of Western Civilization, Religion and Philosophy(Soft) -<u>Soft Cover</u> $24.95 ISBN: 1-884564-56-9

8.   EGYPT AND INDIA (AFRICAN ORIGINS BOOK 3 PART 3) African Origins of Eastern Civilization, Religion, Yoga Mysticism and Philosophy-<u>Soft Cover</u> $29.95 (Soft) ISBN: 1-884564-57-7

9.   THE MYSTERIES OF ISIS: **The Ancient Egyptian Philosophy of Self-Realization** - There are several paths to discover the Divine and the mysteries of the higher Self. This volume details the mystery teachings of the goddess Aset (Isis) from Ancient Egypt- the path of wisdom. It includes the teachings of her temple and the disciplines that are enjoined for the initiates of the temple of Aset as they were given in

ancient times. Also, this book includes the teachings of the main myths of Aset that lead a human being to spiritual enlightenment and immortality. Through the study of ancient myth and the illumination of initiatic understanding the idea of God is expanded from the mythological comprehension to the metaphysical. Then this metaphysical understanding is related to you, the student, so as to begin understanding your true divine nature. ISBN 1-884564-24-0 $22.99

10.   EGYPTIAN PROVERBS: TEMT TCHAAS *Temt Tchaas* means: collection of ——Ancient Egyptian Proverbs How to live according to MAAT Philosophy. Beginning Meditation. All proverbs are indexed for easy searches. For the first time in one volume, ——Ancient Egyptian Proverbs, wisdom teachings and meditations, fully illustrated with hieroglyphic text and symbols. EGYPTIAN PROVERBS is a unique collection of knowledge and wisdom which you can put into practice today and transform your life. 5.5"x 8.5" $14.95 U.S   ISBN: 1-884564-00-3

11.   THE PATH OF DIVINE LOVE The Process of Mystical Transformation and The Path of Divine Love This Volume focuses on the ancient wisdom teachings of "Neter Merri" –the Ancient Egyptian philosophy of Divine Love and how to use them in a scientific process for self-transformation. Love is one of the most powerful human emotions. It is also the source of Divine feeling that unifies God and the individual human being. When love is fragmented and diminished by egoism the Divine connection is lost. The Ancient tradition of Neter Merri leads human beings back to their Divine connection, allowing them to discover their innate glorious self that is actually Divine and immortal. This volume will detail the process of transformation from ordinary consciousness to cosmic consciousness through the integrated practice of the teachings and the path of Devotional Love toward the Divine. 5.5"x 8.5" ISBN 1-884564-11-9 $22.99

12.   INTRODUCTION TO MAAT PHILOSOPHY: Spiritual Enlightenment Through the Path of Virtue Known as Karma Yoga in India, the teachings of MAAT for living virtuously and with orderly wisdom are explained and the student is to begin practicing the precepts of Maat in daily life so as to promote the process of purification of the heart in preparation for the judgment of the soul. This judgment will be understood not as an event that will occur at the time of death but as an event that occurs continuously, at every moment in the life of the individual. The student will learn how to become allied with the forces of the Higher Self and to thereby begin cleansing the mind (heart) of impurities so as to attain a higher vision of reality. ISBN 1-884564-20-8 $22.99

13.   MEDITATION The Ancient Egyptian Path to Enlightenment   Many people do not know about the rich history of meditation practice in Ancient Egypt. This volume outlines the theory of meditation and presents the Ancient Egyptian Hieroglyphic text which give instruction as to the nature of the mind and its three modes of expression. It also presents the texts which give instruction on the practice of meditation for spiritual Enlightenment and unity with the Divine. This volume allows the reader to begin practicing meditation by explaining, in easy to understand terms, the simplest form of meditation and working up to the most advanced form which was practiced in ancient times and which is still practiced by yogis around the world in modern times. ISBN 1-884564-27-7 $24.99

14.   THE GLORIOUS LIGHT MEDITATION Technique of Ancient Egypt ISBN: 1-884564-15-1$14.95 (PB) New for the year 2000. This volume is based on the earliest known instruction in history given for the practice of formal meditation. Discovered by Dr. Muata Ashby, it is inscribed on the walls of the Tomb of Seti I in Thebes Egypt. This volume details the philosophy and practice of this unique system of meditation originated in Ancient Egypt and the earliest practice of meditation known in the world which occurred in the most advanced African Culture.

15.   THE SERPENT POWER: The Ancient Egyptian Mystical Wisdom of the Inner Life Force.   This Volume specifically deals with the latent life Force energy of the universe and in the human body, its control and sublimation. How to develop the Life Force energy of the subtle body. This Volume will introduce the esoteric wisdom of the science of how virtuous living acts in a subtle and mysterious way to cleanse the latent psychic energy conduits and vortices of the spiritual body. ISBN 1-884564-19-4 $22.95

16. EGYPTIAN YOGA MEDITATION IN MOTION Thef Neteru: *The Movement of The Gods and Goddesses* Discover the physical postures and exercises practiced thousands of years ago in Ancient Egypt which are today known as Yoga exercises. This work is based on the pictures and teachings from the Creation story of Ra, The Asarian Resurrection Myth and the carvings and reliefs from various Temples in Ancient Egypt 8.5" X 11" ISBN 1-884564-10-0 Soft Cover $18.99   Exercise video $21.99

17. EGYPTIAN TANTRA YOGA: The Art of Sex Sublimation and Universal Consciousness This Volume will expand on the male and female principles within the human body and in the universe and further detail the sublimation of sexual energy into spiritual energy. The student will study the deities Min and Hathor, Asar and Aset, Geb and Nut and discover the mystical implications for a practical spiritual discipline. This Volume will also focus on the Tantric aspects of Ancient Egyptian and Indian mysticism, the purpose of sex and the mystical teachings of sexual sublimation which lead to self-knowledge and Enlightenment. 5.5"x 8.5" ISBN 1-884564-03-8 $24.95

18. ASARIAN RELIGION: RESURRECTING OSIRIS The path of Mystical Awakening and the Keys to Immortality NEW REVISED AND EXPANDED EDITION!   The Ancient Sages created stories based on human and superhuman beings whose struggles, aspirations, needs and desires ultimately lead them to discover their true Self. The myth of Aset, Asar and Heru is no exception in this area. While there is no one source where the entire story may be found, pieces of it are inscribed in various ancient Temples walls, tombs, steles and papyri. For the first time available, the complete myth of Asar, Aset and Heru has been compiled from original Ancient Egyptian, Greek and Coptic Texts. This epic myth has been richly illustrated with reliefs from the Temple of Heru at Edfu, the Temple of Aset at Philae, the Temple of Asar at Abydos, the Temple of Hathor at Denderah and various papyri, inscriptions and reliefs.   Discover the myth which inspired the teachings of the *Shetaut Neter* (Egyptian Mystery System - Egyptian Yoga) and the Egyptian Book of Coming Forth By Day. Also, discover the three levels of Ancient Egyptian Religion, how to understand the mysteries of the Duat or Astral World and how to discover the abode of the Supreme in the Amenta, *The Other World*   The ancient religion of Asar, Aset and Heru, if properly understood, contains all of the elements necessary to lead the sincere aspirant to attain immortality through inner self-discovery. This volume presents the entire myth and explores the main mystical themes and rituals associated with the myth for understating human existence, creation and the way to achieve spiritual emancipation - *Resurrection.* The Asarian myth is so powerful that it influenced and is still having an effect on the major world religions. Discover the origins and mystical meaning of the Christian Trinity, the Eucharist ritual and the ancient origin of the birthday of Jesus Christ. Soft Cover ISBN: 1-884564-27-5 $24.95

19. THE EGYPTIAN BOOK OF THE DEAD MYSTICISM OF THE PERT EM HERU $26.95   ISBN# 1-884564-28-3 Size: 8½" X 11" I Know myself, I know myself, I am One With God!–From the Pert Em Heru "The Ru Pert em Heru" or "Ancient Egyptian Book of The Dead," or "Book of Coming Forth By Day" as it is more popularly known, has fascinated the world since the successful translation of Ancient Egyptian hieroglyphic scripture over 150 years ago. The astonishing writings in it reveal that the Ancient Egyptians believed in life after death and in an ultimate destiny to discover the Divine. The elegance and aesthetic beauty of the hieroglyphic text itself has inspired many see it as an art form in and of itself. But is there more to it than that? Did the Ancient Egyptian wisdom contain more than just aphorisms and hopes of eternal life beyond death? In this volume Dr. Muata Ashby, the author of over 25 books on Ancient Egyptian Yoga Philosophy has produced a new translation of the original texts which uncovers a mystical teaching underlying the sayings and rituals instituted by the Ancient Egyptian Sages and Saints. "Once the philosophy of Ancient Egypt is understood as a mystical tradition instead of as a religion or primitive mythology, it reveals its secrets which if practiced today will lead anyone to discover the glory of spiritual self-discovery. The Pert em Heru is in every way comparable to the Indian Upanishads or the Tibetan Book of the Dead." Muata Abhaya Ashby

20. ANUNIAN THEOLOGY THE MYSTERIES OF RA The Philosophy of Anu and The Mystical Teachings of The Ancient Egyptian Creation Myth Discover the mystical teachings contained in the Creation Myth and the gods and goddesses who brought creation and human beings into existence. The Creation Myth holds the key to understanding the universe and for attaining spiritual Enlightenment. ISBN: 1-884564-38-0 40 pages $14.95

21. MYSTERIES OF MIND AND MEMPHITE THEOLOGY Mysticism of Ptah, Egyptian Physics and Yoga Metaphysics and the Hidden properties of Matter   This Volume will go deeper into the philosophy of God as creation and will explore the concepts of modern science and how they correlate with ancient teachings. This Volume will lay the ground work for the understanding of the philosophy of universal consciousness and the initiatic/yogic insight into who or what is God? ISBN 1-884564-07-0 $21.95

22. THE GODDESS AND THE EGYPTIAN MYSTERIESTHE PATH OF THE GODDESS THE GODDESS PATH The Secret Forms of the Goddess and the Rituals of Resurrection The Supreme Being may be worshipped as father or as mother. *Ushet Rekhat* or *Mother Worship*, is the spiritual process of worshipping the Divine in the form of the Divine Goddess. It celebrates the most important forms of the Goddess including *Nathor, Maat, Aset, Arat, Amentet and Hathor* and explores their mystical meaning as well as the rising of *Sirius,* the star of Aset (Aset) and the new birth of Hor (Heru). The end of the year is a time of reckoning, reflection and engendering a new or renewed positive movement toward attaining spiritual Enlightenment. The Mother Worship devotional meditation ritual, performed on five days during the month of December and on New Year's Eve, is based on the Ushet Rekhit. During the ceremony, the cosmic forces, symbolized by Sirius - and the constellation of Orion ---, are harnessed through the understanding and devotional attitude of the participant. This propitiation draws the light of wisdom and health to all those who share in the ritual, leading to prosperity and wisdom. $14.95 ISBN 1-884564-18-6

23. *THE MYSTICAL JOURNEY FROM JESUS TO CHRIST* $24.95   ISBN# 1-884564-05-4 size: 8½" X 11" Discover the ancient Egyptian origins of Christianity before the Catholic Church and learn the mystical teachings given by Jesus to assist all humanity in becoming Christlike. Discover the secret meaning of the Gospels that were discovered in Egypt. Also discover how and why so many Christian churches came into being. Discover that the Bible still holds the keys to mystical realization even though its original writings were changed by the church. Discover how to practice the original teachings of Christianity which leads to the Kingdom of Heaven.

24. THE STORY OF ASAR, ASET AND HERU: An Ancient Egyptian Legend (For Children)   Now for the first time, the most ancient myth of Ancient Egypt comes alive for children. Inspired by the books *The Asarian Resurrection: The Ancient Egyptian Bible* and *The Mystical Teachings of The Asarian Resurrection, The Story of Asar, Aset and Heru* is an easy to understand and thrilling tale which inspired the children of Ancient Egypt to aspire to greatness and righteousness. If you and your child have enjoyed stories like *The Lion King* and *Star Wars you will love The Story of Asar, Aset and Heru.* Also, if you know the story of Jesus and Krishna you will discover than Ancient Egypt had a similar myth and that this myth carries important spiritual teachings for living a fruitful and fulfilling life. This book may be used along with *The Parents Guide To The Asarian Resurrection Myth: How to Teach Yourself and Your Child the Principles of Universal Mystical Religion.* The guide provides some background to the Asarian Resurrection myth and it also gives insight into the mystical teachings contained in it which you may introduce to your child. It is designed for parents who wish to grow spiritually with their children and it serves as an introduction for those who would like to study the Asarian Resurrection Myth in depth and to practice its teachings. 41 pages 8.5" X 11"   ISBN: 1-884564-31-3 $12.95

25. THE PARENTS GUIDE TO THE AUSARIAN RESURRECTION MYTH: How to Teach Yourself and Your Child the Principles of Universal Mystical Religion.   This insightful manual brings for the timeless wisdom of the ancient through the Ancient Egyptian myth of Asar, Aset and Heru and the mystical teachings contained in it for parents who want to guide their children to understand and practice the teachings of mystical spirituality. This manual may be used with the children's storybook *The Story of Asar, Aset and Heru* by Dr. Muata Abhaya Ashby. 5.5"x 8.5"   ISBN: 1-884564-30-5 $14.95

26. HEALING THE CRIMINAL HEART BOOK 1 Introduction to Maat Philosophy, Yoga and Spiritual Redemption Through the Path of Virtue   Who is a criminal? Is there such a thing as a criminal heart? What is the source of evil and sinfulness and is there any way to rise above it? Is there redemption for those who have committed sins, even the worst crimes?   Ancient Egyptian mystical psychology holds important answers to these questions. Over ten thousand years ago mystical psychologists, the Sages of Ancient Egypt, studied and charted the human mind and spirit and laid out a path which will lead to

spiritual redemption, prosperity and Enlightenment.   This introductory volume brings forth the teachings of the Asarian Resurrection, the most important myth of Ancient Egypt, with relation to the faults of human existence: anger, hatred, greed, lust, animosity, discontent, ignorance, egoism jealousy, bitterness, and a myriad of psycho-spiritual ailments which keep a human being in a state of negativity and adversity. 5.5"x 8.5"   ISBN: 1-884564-17-8 $15.95

27.   THEATER & DRAMA OF THE ANCIENT EGYPTIAN MYSTERIES: Featuring the Ancient Egyptian stage play-"The Enlightenment of Hathor' Based on an Ancient Egyptian Drama, The original Theater - Mysticism of the Temple of Hetheru $14.95 By Dr. Muata Ashby

28.   GUIDE TO PRINT ON DEMAND: SELF-PUBLISH FOR PROFIT, SPIRITUAL FULFILLMENT AND SERVICE TO HUMANITY Everyone asks us how we produced so many books in such a short time. Here are the secrets to writing and producing books that uplift humanity and how to get them printed for a fraction of the regular cost. Anyone can become an author even if they have limited funds. All that is necessary is the willingness to learn how the printing and book business work and the desire to follow the special instructions given here for preparing your manuscript format. Then you take your work directly to the non-traditional companies who can produce your books for less than the traditional book printer can. ISBN: 1-884564-40-2 $16.95 U. S.

29.   Egyptian Mysteries: Vol. 1, Shetaut Neter ISBN: 1-884564-41-0 $19.99 What are the Mysteries? For thousands of years the spiritual tradition of Ancient Egypt, S*hetaut Neter,* "The Egyptian Mysteries," "The Secret Teachings," have fascinated, tantalized and amazed the world. At one time exalted and recognized as the highest culture of the world, by Africans, Europeans, Asiatics, Hindus, Buddhists and other cultures of the ancient world, in time it was shunned by the emerging orthodox world religions. Its temples desecrated, its philosophy maligned, its tradition spurned, its philosophy dormant in the mystical *Medu Neter*, the mysterious hieroglyphic texts which hold the secret symbolic meaning that has scarcely been discerned up to now. What are the secrets of *Nehast* {spiritual awakening and emancipation, resurrection}. More than just a literal translation, this volume is for awakening to the secret code *Shetitu* of the teaching which was not deciphered by Egyptologists, nor could be understood by ordinary spiritualists. This book is a reinstatement of the original science made available for our times, to the reincarnated followers of Ancient Egyptian culture and the prospect of spiritual freedom to break the bonds of *Khemn*, "ignorance," and slavery to evil forces: *Såaa* .

30.   EGYPTIAN MYSTERIES VOL 2: Dictionary of Gods and Goddesses ISBN: 1-884564-23-2 $21.95 This book is about the mystery of neteru, the gods and goddesses of Ancient Egypt (Kamit, Kemet). Neteru means "Gods and Goddesses." But the Neterian teaching of Neteru represents more than the usual limited modern day concept of "divinities" or "spirits." The Neteru of Kamit are also metaphors, cosmic principles and vehicles for the enlightening teachings of Shetaut Neter (Ancient Egyptian-African Religion). Actually they are the elements for one of the most advanced systems of spirituality ever conceived in human history. Understanding the concept of neteru provides a firm basis for spiritual evolution and the pathway for viable culture, peace on earth and a healthy human society.   Why is it important to have gods and goddesses in our lives? In order for spiritual evolution to be possible, once a human being has accepted that there is existence after death and there is a transcendental being who exists beyond time and space knowledge, human beings need a connection to that which transcends the ordinary experience of human life in time and space and a means to understand the transcendental reality beyond the mundane reality.

31.   EGYPTIAN MYSTERIES VOL. 3 The Priests and Priestesses of Ancient Egypt ISBN: 1-884564-53-4 $22.95 This volume details the path of Neterian priesthood, the joys, challenges and rewards of advanced Neterian life, the teachings that allowed the priests and priestesses to manage the most long lived civilization in human history and how that path can be adopted today; for those who want to tread the path of the Clergy of Shetaut Neter.

32.   THE KING OF EGYPT: The Struggle of Good and Evil for Control of the World and The Human Soul ISBN 1-8840564-44-5 $18.95   Have you seen movies like The Lion King, Hamlet, The Odyssey, or The Little Buddha? These have been some of the most popular movies in modern times. The Sema Institute of

Yoga is dedicated to researching and presenting the wisdom and culture of ancient Africa. The Script is designed to be produced as a motion picture but may be addapted for the theater as well. 160 pages bound or unbound (specify with your order) $19.95 copyright 1998 By Dr. Muata Ashby

33. FROM EGYPT TO GREECE: The Kamitan Origins of Greek Culture and Religion ISBN: 1-884564-47-X $22.95 U.S. FROM EGYPT TO GREECE This insightful manual is a quick reference to Ancient Egyptian mythology and philosophy and its correlation to what later became known as Greek and Rome mythology and philosophy. It outlines the basic tenets of the mythologies and shoes the ancient origins of Greek culture in Ancient Egypt. This volume also acts as a resource for Colleges students who would like to set up fraternities and sororities based on the original Ancient Egyptian principles of Sheti and Maat philosophy. ISBN: 1-884564-47-X $22.95 U.S.

34. THE FORTY TWO PRECEPTS OF MAAT, THE PHILOSOPHY OF RIGHTEOUS ACTION AND THE ANCIENT EGYPTIAN WISDOM TEXTS ADVANCED STUDIES This manual is designed for use with the 1998 Maat Philosophy Class conducted by Dr. Muata Ashby. This is a detailed study of Maat Philosophy. It contains a compilation of the 42 laws or precepts of Maat and the corresponding principles which they represent along with the teachings of the ancient Egyptian Sages relating to each. Maat philosophy was the basis of Ancient Egyptian society and government as well as the heart of Ancient Egyptian myth and spirituality. Maat is at once a goddess, a cosmic force and a living social doctrine, which promotes social harmony and thereby paves the way for spiritual evolution in all levels of society. ISBN: 1-884564-48-8 $16.95 U.S.

Music Based on the Prt M Hru and other Kemetic Texts

Available on Compact Disc $14.99 and Audio Cassette $9.99

Adorations to the Goddess

Music for Worship of the Goddess

NEW Egyptian Yoga Music CD
by Sehu Maa
Ancient Egyptian Music CD
Instrumental Music played on reproductions of Ancient Egyptian Instruments– Ideal for meditation and reflection on the Divine and for the practice of spiritual programs and Yoga exercise sessions.

©1999 By Muata Ashby

CD $14.99 –

MERIT'S INSPIRATION
NEW Egyptian Yoga Music CD
by Sehu Maa
Ancient Egyptian Music CD
Instrumental Music played on
reproductions of Ancient Egyptian Instruments– Ideal for <u>meditation</u> and
reflection on the Divine and for the practice of spiritual programs and <u>Yoga exercise sessions.</u>
©1999 By
Muata Ashby
CD $14.99 –
UPC# 761527100429

ANORATIONS TO RA AND HETHERU
NEW Egyptian Yoga Music CD
By Sehu Maa (Muata Ashby)
Based on the Words of Power of Ra and HetHeru
played on reproductions of Ancient Egyptian Instruments **Ancient Egyptian Instruments used: Voice, Clapping, Nefer Lute, Tar Drum, Sistrums, Cymbals** – The Chants, Devotions, Rhythms and Festive Songs Of the Neteru
– Ideal for meditation, and devotional singing and dancing.
©1999 By Muata Ashby
CD $14.99 –
UPC# 761527100221

SONGS TO ASAR ASET AND HERU
NEW
Egyptian Yoga Music CD
By Sehu Maa

played on reproductions of Ancient Egyptian Instruments– The Chants, Devotions, Rhythms and Festive Songs Of the Neteru - Ideal for meditation, and devotional singing and dancing.

Based on the Words of Power of Asar (Asar), Aset (Aset) and Heru (Heru) Om Asar Aset Heru is the third in a series of musical explorations of the Kemetic (Ancient Egyptian) tradition of music. Its ideas are based on the Ancient Egyptian Religion of Asar, Aset and Heru and it is designed for listening, meditation and worship. ©1999 By Muata Ashby

CD $14.99 –
UPC# 761527100122

HAARI OM: ANCIENT EGYPT MEETS INDIA IN MUSIC
NEW Music CD
By Sehu Maa

The Chants, Devotions, Rhythms and Festive Songs Of the Ancient Egypt and India, harmonized and played on reproductions of ancient instruments along with modern instruments and beats. Ideal for meditation, and devotional singing and dancing.

Haari Om is the fourth in a series of musical explorations of the Kemetic (Ancient Egyptian) and Indian traditions of music, chanting and devotional spiritual practice. Its ideas are based on the Ancient Egyptian Yoga spirituality and Indian Yoga spirituality.

©1999 By Muata Ashby
CD $14.99 –
UPC# 761527100528

RA AKHU: THE GLORIOUS LIGHT
NEW
Egyptian Yoga Music CD
By Sehu Maa
The fifth collection of original music compositions based on the Teachings and Words of The Trinity, the God Asar and the Goddess Nebethet, the Divinity Aten, the God Heru, and the Special Meditation Hekau or Words of Power of Ra from the Ancient Egyptian Tomb of Seti I and more...
played on reproductions of Ancient Egyptian Instruments and modern instruments - **Ancient Egyptian Instruments used: Voice, Clapping, Nefer Lute, Tar Drum, Sistrums, Cymbals**
– The Chants, Devotions, Rhythms and Festive Songs Of the Neteru – Ideal for meditation, and devotional singing and dancing.
©1999 By Muata Ashby
CD $14.99 –
UPC# 761527100825

GLORIES OF THE DIVINE MOTHER
Based on the hieroglyphic text of the worship of Goddess Net.
The Glories of The Great Mother
©2000 Muata Ashby
CD $14.99 UPC# 761527101129`

Order Form

Telephone orders: Call Toll Free: 1(305) 378-6253. Have your AMEX, Optima, Visa or MasterCard ready.

Fax orders: 1-(305) 378-6253   E-MAIL ADDRESS: Semayoga@aol.com

Postal Orders: Sema Institute of Yoga, P.O. Box 570459, Miami, Fl. 33257. USA.

Please send the following books and / or tapes.

ITEM

_____Cost $_____

_____Cost $_____

_____Cost $_____

_____Cost $_____

_____Cost $_____

Total $_____

Name:_____

Physical Address:_____

City:_____ State:_____ Zip:_____

Sales tax: Please add 6.5% for books shipped to Florida addresses

_____Shipping: $6.50 for first book and .50¢ for each additional

_____Shipping: Outside US $5.00 for first book and $3.00 for each additional

_____Payment:_____

_____Check -Include Driver License #:

_____

_____Credit card: _____ Visa, _____ MasterCard, _____ Optima, _____ AMEX.

Card number:_____

Name on card:_____ Exp. date:_____/_____

Copyright 1995-2005 Dr. R. Muata Abhaya Ashby
Sema Institute of Yoga
P.O.Box 570459, Miami, Florida, 33257
(305) 378-6253 Fax: (305) 378-6253

8645548R0

Made in the USA
Charleston, SC
30 June 2011